C000174859

Getting into
Engineering Courses

Getting into guides

Getting into

Engineering Courses

James Burnett

2nd edition

ADAMS GRAMMAR SCHOOL
LIBRARY

Getting into Engineering Courses

This second edition published in 2013 by Trotman Publishing, an imprint of Crimson Publishing, Westminster House, Kew Road, Richmond, Surrey TW9 2ND.

© Trotman Publishing 2013

Author: James Burnett

620·007 1st edition by James Burnett, published in 2011

British Library Cataloguing in Publication Data
A catalogue record of this book is available from the British Library.

ISBN: 978 1 90604 189 2

All rights reserved. This book is sold subject to the condition that it shall not, by way of trade or otherwise, be lent, resold, hired out or otherwise circulated without the publisher's prior written consent in any form of binding or cover other than that in which it is published and without a similar condition including this condition being imposed on the subsequent purchaser. No part of this publication may be reproduced, stored in a retrieval system or transmitted in any form or by any means, electronic and mechanical, photocopying, recording or otherwise without prior permission of Crimson Publishing.

Typeset by IDSUK (DataConnection) Ltd
Printed and bound in the UK by TJ International Ltd, Padstow, Cornwall

Contents

Contents

About the author

James Burnett is a university adviser at Mander Portman Woodward. He has written and edited a number of the Trotman/MPW guides including *Getting into Art & Design Courses* and *Getting into Business & Economics Courses*. He delivers seminars and workshops throughout the world on UK university entrance, the most recent being in Malaysia, China, Thailand and Singapore.

Acknowledgements

I would like to thank all of the people who helped me in writing this book, including Barry Sullivan, Head of Admissions at Cardiff School of Engineering, Dolly Duan, Holly Ivins, Dominic Joyeux and Isabelle Kihm from, respectively, the Royal Academy of Engineering and the Institution of Mechanical Engineers; Emma Weeks from Bristol University; and Professor Stepan Lucyszyn from Imperial College. Thank you also to Georgina Le Vavasseur dit Durell, Nur Farah Ani Wan Hassan, Ben Goodrich, Alexandra Jackson, Josh Flower and Gulnaz Niyazova, and to Nigel Brook. I am grateful for the assistance of UCAS and to the universities that contributed advice or information.

James Burnett

Introduction

Engineering touches all aspects of our lives. Some of the work of engineers is easy to see and to understand – the electricity supply to your home, the car that drives you to school, the iPod you listen to on the way, the roads and bridges that take you to your destination, the school building and the classroom furniture you use, the water supply, the packaging for the food you eat at lunchtime, the computer you use to help you with your homework . . . the list is endless. But there are other aspects of engineering that you may not have thought about. Engineers also deal with financial and business issues, for example looking at the cost-effectiveness of manufacturing products; and many engineers run their own businesses. Engineers are closely involved in environmental and safety issues, as well as helping to shape the world's future energy and raw material needs.

Those of you who watched the 2012 London Olympic Games opening ceremony will have noticed the celebration of the UK's unique relationship with engineering and technology, from Isambard Kingdom Brunel, who pioneered some of the world's greatest engineering projects in the nineteenth century, to Tim Berners-Lee (the inventor of the World Wide Web). However, engineers are not always portrayed as glamorous figures. The public perception is of the person in oil-stained overalls wearing a hard hat and a luminous jacket, very often called in when there are problems (oil spills, power cuts, and damaged buildings and bridges spring to mind). There are not many films that have engineers as their leading characters (except for a string of blockbuster disaster movies from the 1970s), and when most people think about, for example, a stunning new building, it is the architect's name that comes to mind rather than the structural engineers who made it possible; when Apple introduces a new iPhone, we read articles about the queues outside the shops rather than about the electronic and materials engineers who created it; and as you browse the web and come across an exciting website, you praise the web designer rather than the software engineers who developed the program that allowed the designers to weave their magic.

As you are reading this introduction, you are probably thinking about what opportunities exist for engineers. I hope that reading this book coupled with your research into universities and careers within engineering will show you that there is a myriad of exciting possibilities waiting for you within this field.

About this book

The aim of this book is to take you through the process of applying to study engineering, from choosing courses and universities through to postgraduate courses and career opportunities.

Chapter 1 focuses on what studying engineering at university entails. Then in Chapters 2, 3 and 4 we look at the desirability of gaining work experience and how to go about finding suitable placements, how to choose the right engineering course for you, and how to apply for undergraduate courses using the UCAS system. In Chapters 5 and 6 we focus on two specific areas of the application, the UCAS personal statement and the interview, and how to use these to make the best possible impression on the university selectors.

Chapter 7 contains advice for mature applicants and those who are applying from outside the UK. In Chapter 8 there is a breakdown of the options available when you get your examination results and what to do if you do not achieve the grades you require. Financial information, both the cost of studying and what financial support may be available, is covered in Chapter 9. Chapter 10 looks at options for further study and training for graduates. In Chapter 11 there are lists of sources of further information for potential engineers, and at the end there is a glossary of common terms used in this book.

You can use this book as a source of advice and information by reading the chapters or sections that are of relevance to you. However, I recommend that you read the book from the beginning rather than dipping in and out of it, because you will then get a more complete picture.

References to university entrance requirements throughout the book are usually given in terms of A level or AS level grades, and the equivalent entry requirements for students studying Cambridge Pre-U, the International Baccalaureate (IB), Scottish Highers and other qualifications are given in the UCAS tariff in Chapter 11. The universities, on their websites, will provide further details of entrance requirements for all of the commonly accepted examinations, and the 'Course search' facility on the UCAS website (www.ucas.com) will also list these. Regardless of the examination system you are using, the advice on applications given in the book is applicable to all candidates. If you have any questions about your own particular situation, the universities are happy to deal with individual queries and can be contacted via their 'Contact us' sections on their websites.

Engineering defined

What is engineering?

What is the difference between science and engineering? There are many definitions, but, essentially, engineering is the practical application of mathematics and science to create machines, processes or structures. Whereas the starting point in science generally involves trying to explain or predict phenomena through the development and verification of theories and models, engineering is the process of physically achieving a goal by applying scientific ideas and theories in a practical way.

What do engineers do?

Although we tend to classify engineers and engineering courses under different headings, there is a good deal of overlap, and most engineering projects or processes require the input of many different types of engineer. When you look in more detail at the course content of different engineering programmes, you will see that there are many common elements to these. For instance, mechanical engineers will spend time studying electronic and electrical engineering as machines often use electricity as a power source; and civil engineering requires an understanding of the properties of materials, as does structural engineering.

Mechanical engineers

Mechanical engineers work in the development and manufacture of machines. This is obviously a very broad description: the word 'machine' covers an enormous range of devices, from medical equipment that is used to perform microsurgery through to aircraft carriers. Mechanical engineering courses include a number of specialist areas, such as aeronautical engineering and automotive engineering. Aeronautical engineers work on all aspects of aircraft and spacecraft, from aerodynamics to the design of engines. Automotive engineers can also work on things that fly as well as cars and other forms of transport.

Electrical and electronic engineers

Electrical and electronic engineers work with electrical and electronic devices. As with mechanical engineering, these range from a microscopic scale (integrated circuits or solid state devices, for example) through to national electricity networks. Many universities offer a joint electrical/electronic engineering course, but it is also possible to specialise in just one of these subjects. There are close links between electronic engineering and computer or information technology (IT) engineering.

Information systems engineers

Information systems engineering is closely linked to electronic engineering. It focuses on computer systems and the transfer of electronic and digital information – mobile phones, the internet, and computer operating systems.

Civil engineers

Civil engineering deals with the large-scale infrastructure that is an essential part of daily life, such as roads, bridges, dams, water supplies, and office and apartment blocks. (The name civil engineering came about in order to differentiate projects that were there to benefit society in general from military engineering projects.)

Structural engineers

Structural engineering deals with the use and suitability of materials that are intended for creating structures such as buildings, bridges, sporting facilities and electricity pylons. The discipline covers the structure and properties of materials on a microscopic level, and the behaviour of structures on a macroscopic scale. Structural engineers work closely with civil engineers and with architects. For example, once an architect has come up with a design for a new office block, structural engineers look at what materials will be required to ensure that the project is feasible, before handing it over to the civil engineers to build it.

Materials engineers

Material engineering is closely related to structural engineering in that it looks at the properties of materials that are necessary to create structures. However, it also covers the use of materials for other requirements, such as plastics, ceramics, glass and polymers. A mobile phone manufacturer, for example, may work with materials engineers to ensure that the phone is strong enough to withstand daily knocks while at the same time being light and attractive.

Chemical engineers

Chemical engineering deals with the industrial processes that produce, for example, drugs, food and fuels. Chemical engineers are not only concerned with the chemical properties of the materials they are producing or developing, but also the economic and safety aspects of the projects. Chemical engineering links closely with bioengineering, biomedical engineering and biotechnology.

Biomedical engineers

Biomedical engineering (along with biotechnology) looks at the engineering aspects of living things, often for medical purposes. This can range from working with living materials, such as animal tissue, to the development of medical instrumentation (medical scanners and equipment used in surgery), and the design of machines and devices such as heart pace-makers and artificial limbs.

Petroleum engineers

Petroleum engineering covers all aspects of the oil, gas and petroleum industries – from exploration and excavation, through refining and purifi-cation, to distribution. It covers geological studies, the chemical proper-ties of hydrocarbons, and industrial processes.

Design and product engineers

Design and product engineering deals with the process of creating and developing systems and devices. As well as looking at production pro-cesses, such as the design of production lines and factories, design and product engineers have to be aware of safety and cost issues. As an example, take a new car, the production of which involves mechanical and electrical engineering input, computer hardware and software development, the choice of the right materials to ensure that the car will be safe, functional and attractive, and the creation of a production line that will be both efficient and cost-effective.

There are many other classifications of engineering disciplines and courses (see page 25), and there are subsets of some of the areas mentioned above and courses that combine two or more of these disci-plines. So, you will need to spend some time researching possible courses before deciding what you want to do. Advice on this can be found in Chapter 3.

Most engineering projects involve the input of a range of specialisms (see Figures 1 and 2).

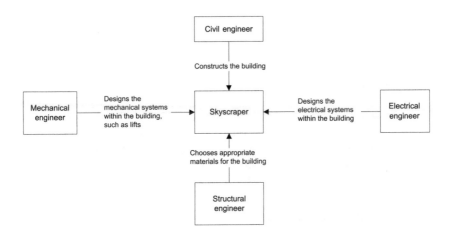

Figure 1: Input into building a skyscraper

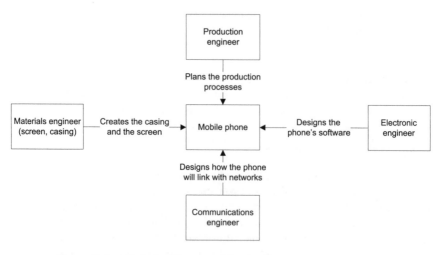

Figure 2: Input into building a mobile phone

Opportunities for engineers

Very few careers provide as many opportunities as engineering while at the same time offering secure employment prospects.

- Engineers can work anywhere in the world.
- The work can be theoretical or practical, and can be carried out within an office or on-site.
- Engineers can work for multinational companies or set up their own business.
- Engineers can work on any scale, from nanotechnology and micro-electronics, through to building the world's biggest structures.

Case studies

The Royal Academy of Engineering has launched a campaign, 'Shape the Future', which is aimed at students who are thinking about a career in engineering. As part of this campaign, the organisation has produced a series of case studies, which are essential reading for anyone con-templating studying engineering. You can access the booklet on the Academy's website (www.raeng.org.uk/education/stf/pdf/tsz_fok_booklet.pdf). The Institution of Mechanical Engineers also publishes case histories on its website (www.imeche.org).

Working internationally

Few careers provide greater opportunities to work or study overseas, and this is one of the attractions of engineering. Many of the world's major engineering projects are undertaken by multinational companies, and many engineers work freelance, choosing their projects and locations to suit their skills and circumstances. The rapid technological advances of the BRIC nations (Brazil, Russia, India and China) have created enormous demands for qualified engineers.

Case study

From Plymouth to paddy fields

Graduating with a degree in civil engineering from Plymouth in 1980, I returned to the north of England to continue my training towards the institution professional examination. My company of choice was an engineering consultancy with a long pedigree in the design, project management and supervision of power station construction. Based in Manchester, the next 10 years provided formative experience in major projects around the globe, including power stations in the UK, Isle of Man, Ireland, Greece and India; coastal protection works and desalination plants in the Middle East; and roads, bridges, harbour and jetty design in the UK. This included three years of on-site construction supervision of highway and power station projects.

The following six years provided opportunity to work with a number of renowned UK-based consulting engineers while specialising in the design of bridge works and other major highway structures. In 1996 I was given my first opportunity to work overseas. This was for a small Australian consulting service in Oman, responsible for projects ranging from highway feasibility studies in Pakistan to design and construction of the local Hyatt Hotel and the Royal Sports Stadium. The following years provided further opportunities to practise in my chosen fields of bridge, marine and power station engineering, including project management of the Incheon Bridge in South Korea, the sixth largest cable-stayed span in the world.

My current role is in Vietnam, helping to develop the country's infrastructure in terms of new power station design and construction. As the lead civil owner's engineer, my team is responsible for the design and construction review of a 1,200MW power station in rural Vietnam.

Nigel Brook BSc CEng MICE

Competition for places

While the ratio of applicants to places for engineering courses is lower than for many other subjects (see below), the competition for places at the higher ranked universities is intense. Thus many candidates, while being successful at gaining a place on an engineering degree course, do so either through Clearing or at one of their lower preference universities. You should aim as high as you can (within the boundaries set by your examination results and predictions) in terms of your choice of university, as employers will look not only at what you studied but where you studied. Therefore do all that you can to ensure that your choice of university will stand you in good stead in the future.

UCAS (www.ucas.com) reports that for 2011 entry, around 31,000 students applied for 25,000 places. Of these, approximately one in every eight applications were from women, although women had a higher success rate in gaining places (nearly 85% were successful compared with 78% of men). International students were less successful in gaining places than their UK counterparts – 2,100 of the 3,100 EU applicants were successful, along with 4,400 of the 6,900 non-EU international students. The ratio of applicants to places varies from course to course. For example, the success rate for civil engineering applicants was around 80%, whereas 92% of electrical and electronic engineering applicants gained places.

As with most things in life, the more planning and preparation you do, the better your chances of success. This is, of course, true for your studies and examinations; but it is also the case that research and a well-planned UCAS application will give you a much better chance of being made offers by your chosen universities. This applies to all aspects of the application: choosing your courses and universities, looking at their entrance requirements, writing a personal statement that will demonstrate your seriousness about, and suitability for, the course, and ensuring that you are prepared for any interviews or entrance tests.

Ignore those who tell you that 'if you are lucky, you will get an offer' – if you pitch your applications at the level that is appropriate for your qualifications (past and predicted) and prepare properly, you can remove most of the uncertainty from your application. The following chapters will tell you how to do this.

1 | Studying engineering

What does studying engineering actually entail? Is it all practical work? How much mathematics is involved? Should I take a joint honours degree? This chapter covers these and many other questions. Once you have read the chapter, my advice is to go to the university websites as they will provide you with more detail as well as case histories and comments from current and past students.

Case study

The hours involved in engineering can seem daunting but the rewards are the experiences and the people you meet along the way. At Cardiff there are evenings of design, make and test, sponsored by major engineering institutes – these are good for networking and making friends in a relaxed environment. Engineering is a course which keeps you on your toes; it is a degree which is linked to the outside world. Engineering at Cardiff has such a group atmosphere and everyone here is willing to help everyone else out – from the lecturers creating extra study sessions to your friends studying together. This atmosphere has helped me succeed in my first year and now I am confident that the years to come will be equally good.

Georgina Le Vavasseur dit Durell, Student, Cardiff School of Engineering, Cardiff University

---

Engineering courses

The structure of an engineering course will not only vary from discipline to discipline, but also from university to university. The common elements to all engineering courses are:

- mathematics (see page 11)
- physical laws (for example Newton's laws or the laws of energy conservation or thermodynamics)
- the physics of materials (physical, electrical and thermal properties)
- environmental, safety and health issues
- cost and other economic issues.

Look at the course content in detail on the university websites to ensure that your interests are covered. Two examples of the range of topics covered as part of an engineering degree are shown in the following boxes. The first gives the programme structure of the civil engineering course at Bristol University.

Civil engineering at Bristol University

Year 1

Engineering mathematics
Properties of materials
Structural engineering
Geotechnics
Fluid mechanics
Systems and surveying
Design and computing
One from: thermodynamics; electronics; sustainable development

Year 2

Engineering mathematics
Structures and materials
Geotechnics
Hydraulics
Computational modelling
Professional studies
Civil engineering design
One from: systems and technologies for smart cities; other options

Year 3

Structural engineering
Geotechnics
Water engineering
Civil engineering systems
Professional studies
Water resources project
Scheme design
Research project
Plus options from: slopes and dams; seismic analysis; sustainable construction

Source: www.bristol.ac.uk

The second box shows the programme structure of the University College London (UCL) electronic and electrical engineering course.

Electronic and electrical engineering at UCL

Year 1

Electronic circuits
Circuit analysis and synthesis
Digital circuits
Object-orientated programming
Electromagnetics
Mathematics for electronic engineers
Communications systems
Engineering design principles

Year 2

Circuit analysis and synthesis
Optoelectronics
Electronic circuits
Fields and waves in electronic systems
Digital IC (integrated circuit) design
Semiconductor devices
Object-orientated programming
Mathematics for electronic engineers

Year 3

Project
Further courses from a selection of options

Source: www.ucl.ac.uk

The importance of mathematics

All engineers use mathematical methods as an integral part of their work. While much of engineering relies on physical processes to develop and produce devices, machines, structures, fuels or chemicals, these are all underpinned by mathematical calculations and models. If you look at the course outlines for engineering degrees you will notice that a significant amount of the first-year content involves mathematics. Most universities will specify an A level (or equivalent) mathematics grade in their entrance requirements, so if you are interested in becoming an engineer you will need to study mathematics. If you want to be involved in production or design but do not want to study mathematics, you could look at alternative courses such as product design.

Very few universities require students to have an A level in further mathematics or the equivalent in order to be considered for engineering courses.

Methods of assessment and study

Most universities award degrees on the basis of examinations that are sat throughout the course, although the weightings between examinations sat in the different years of the course may vary from university to university. Most engineering courses also involve coursework, dissertations or practical assessments. Details are given on the university websites. Courses will also contain different amounts of laboratory or practical work, work placements with engineering companies, or on-site work experience. This will also be detailed in the course outlines on the university websites and so you can make sure that your chosen course suits your own preferences or requirements before applying. Teaching is normally conducted through lectures (sometimes supplemented by one-to-one tutorials) or laboratory workshops.

Combined honours courses

There are a number of joint or combined honours degrees available, but there is less flexibility with engineering courses than there might be with arts or humanities subjects. This is simply because engineering degrees tend to lead towards careers in engineering, and so they focus on this.

Many engineers end up running their own engineering company or business, or taking a managerial role within an engineering firm, and so a wide range of degrees that combine engineering with management are available.

As an example, we will look at the MEng Electrical and Electronic Engineering with Management course at Imperial College, London.

MEng with Management course elements, Imperial College, London

Year 1

- Analogue electronics
- Analysis of circuits
- Digital electronics
- Energy conversion
- Introduction to signals and communications
- Mathematics
- Semiconductor physics
- Software engineering
- Professional development

Year 2

- Algorithms and data structures
- Analogue electronics
- Communications
- Control engineering
- Digital electronics

- Power engineering
- Fields and devices
- Introduction to computer architecture

- Mathematics
- Signals and linear systems
- A non-technical subject
- Optional modules

Year 3

Three business and five electronic or electrical engineering modules

Year 4 (MEng)

Three business and four technical modules, plus either one non-technical or one technical module

Source: www.imperial.ac.uk

You will notice that the programme for the first two years of the MEng course at Imperial College concentrates on the theoretical and technical aspects of electrical and electronic engineering. In the third and fourth years (there are four years because this is an MEng, not a BEng course, see page 101) there is more flexibility for you to steer the degree towards your own interests, and you would study business courses alongside the engineering courses.

If you intend to apply for a joint or combined honours course, you must ensure that your personal statement addresses both aspects of the course (see page 42).

Other courses

Foundation degrees

Foundation degrees are two-year full-time (or three-year part-time or distance learning) courses that are provided by some universities. (Do not confuse these with the foundation courses offered to some international students in place of A levels or the equivalent.) They are intended for students who do not have conventional academic back-grounds, for example students who left school after taking their GCSEs and have been working in a relevant field, or mature applicants. Many employers will accept Foundation degrees as an acceptable qualifica-tion; and there are many opportunities for students with a Foundation degree to follow this with an extra year of university study to gain a bachelor's degree. You can apply for Foundation degrees through UCAS (www.ucas.com). Subjects available at Foundation degree level include all the major engineering fields, and some specialist ones (such as Northampton University's lift engineering course, which is a three-year distance learning course).

Higher national diplomas

Higher national diplomas (HNDs) are usually two-year courses, often equivalent to, or taught simultaneously with, the first two years of a bachelor's degree. Students who are successful on the HND course can study for a third year to gain a bachelor's degree. Entrance requirements are normally less stringent than for a degree. For example, Coventry University asks for 260 UCAS tariff points from three A levels (including A level mathematics and/or physics) for entrance onto some degree-level courses, but only 200 points from two A levels, with no subject requirements, for the equivalent HND course.

Scottish degree courses

Undergraduate degree courses at Scottish universities leading to bachelor's degree qualifications are four years in duration, although it is sometimes possible to enter in year two. This is sometimes called 'Advanced Entry' and the advantage of this is that it reduces the course length to three years for a BEng course or four years for the MEng course. The Scottish universities that offer this option will specify the entry requirements for the second-year (level 2) entry on their websites. The grade or score requirements are generally higher than for the first-year (level 1) entry. For example, Dundee University asks for ABB at A level or 32 points at IB for first-year entry onto the electronic and electrical engineering course, and AAB or 34 IB points for entry into the second year.

The course structure of the four-year degree allows students to study a broader range of subjects in the first year, compared with what is on offer in the three-year degrees common in England, Wales and Northern Ireland. The MEng qualification (see page 101) normally takes five years in Scottish universities.

2 | Getting work experience

Work experience is an invaluable way of demonstrating to the universities that you are committed to the course you are applying for. It also shows that you have researched how engineers translate their academic studies into the practical skills that are required in the real world. Work experience will also show you whether you are suitable for a career in engineering, and what qualities are needed in a successful engineer. One of the things that an admissions tutor will look for is how serious you are about your chosen course. By writing about your work experience and how what you saw relates to what you enjoy studying or to things that you have read about, you can show the selectors that you have thought about engineering as a whole and as a potential career, rather than as an academic discipline only.

Recent surveys have highlighted the importance that engineering employers attach to internships and work experience. And this is also true of your university application. As more and more students chase a fixed number of places, preference is given to those candidates who can demonstrate that they have made an effort to find out what working within the field of engineering will be like.

What will you gain from work experience?

- You will have lots to write about in your UCAS personal statement, and you will be able to demonstrate your research into the profession.
- It will help you to decide which area of engineering is most suitable for you. Do you want to work outside or in an office? On practical problems or on the theoretical side of the subject? In a small business or a large multinational company?
- The contacts that you make during your work experience may be helpful in your future career.

Looking for work experience

Where to start

You may be fortunate in that your school will arrange this for you as part of a work-experience scheme. If not, then you will need to look for placements yourself.

So how do you get work experience?

- You could approach local companies or use any contacts that your family may have.
- The institutes of engineering have contacts with engineering companies so try to go through them (see contact details in Chapter 11).
- There are many schemes operated by universities and the engineering institutes aimed at attracting students into engineering, and these often involve work placements.

If you know someone, or of someone, in a local engineering firm, try asking to go in for one or two weeks' work experience or work-shadowing during the holidays. Remember that even a single day of work-shadowing is better than no evidence of experience within the workplace, and something even tangentially related to engineering is better than no work experience at all. Helping organise the files for a local car mechanic would give you some access to the practicalities of engineering problems, and would be a good stimulus for reading more about automotive engineering, for example.

How to apply for work experience

You need to prepare a curriculum vitae (CV), sometimes called a résumé. This should be short and to the point, outlining your education, experiences, achievements and contact details. It should be word-processed on plain paper (but can be accompanied by a handwritten letter), and it should not be longer than two sides.

Your CV should include:

- full name, address, telephone number and email address
- date of birth
- nationality
- education – places, qualifications and grades (start with the most recent)
- skills (e.g. computer skills, software packages you are familiar with, languages spoken, whether you hold a driving licence)
- work experience (full time or part time, with names and addresses of the companies or businesses and a brief description of your responsibilities)
- positions of responsibility
- hobbies
- names and contact details of two or three people who can act as your referees.

Points to remember:

- highlight any experiences or achievements that are relevant to engineering
- highlight any skills gained (teamwork, communication, responsibilities)
- ensure that the layout makes it easy to read
- check all spelling and grammar carefully
- make sure there are no gaps in the CV (periods of time that are unaccounted for).

A sample CV

Lay out your CV clearly and logically, avoiding gaps, and including any exams you are studying for as well as those taken. Below is an example.

Jonathan Luke

Address: 1 Cameron Road, Richmond, London TW9 1MB

Telephone: 0123 456 7890
Email: jl@whizzmail.co.uk

Date of birth: 1 January 1995
Nationality: British

Education
2006–13: Richmond High School
2013: A levels to be taken: Physics, Chemistry, Mathematics
2012: AS level: Geography (B)
2011: GCSEs: English (A), Mathematics (A), Geography (A), German (A), Biology (B), Chemistry (B), History (C), Physics (C)

Work experience
2011–13 (Saturdays)
Sales Assistant in Heggie's Department Store.
Responsible for operating the checkouts during busy times; dealing with customer enquiries and complaints; checking till receipts against takings.
The job requires good communication skills, the ability to deal sympathetically with complaints, and accuracy in dealing with the financial aspects of the post.

Skills
Modern languages: good written and spoken German.

IT: competent in MS Word, PowerPoint and Excel; good keyboard skills.

Positions of responsibility
Captain of school volleyball team; treasurer for the school film society.

Interests
Volleyball, swimming, reading, film, travel and music.

References
Available on request.

The covering letter

The covering letter (often handwritten, unless the company asks for a word-processed letter) should add more detail to the CV and also explain why the post you are applying for is suitable for you. You should find out the name of the person who will read it, and refer to them by name. If you use the person's name, sign off with 'Yours sincerely'. If for some reason you need to address it to an unknown person, then use 'Dear Sir' or 'Dear Madam' and end it with 'Yours faithfully'.

A sample covering letter is shown below.

Ms H McIntosh
Head of Personnel
Scout Engineering
St John's Road
Edinburgh

23 January 2013

Dear Ms McIntosh

I am interested in applying for a part-time post at Scout Engineering, to gain some work experience in preparation for my application for a degree course at Haddington University. I am particularly interested in your company because of its specialism in GPS systems, which is something I have been researching as part of my International Baccalaureate studies, for my extended essay. I am hoping to study electronic engineering at university next year.

In addition to my qualifications shown on the attached CV, I have been working part-time in my local charity shop and I am often left in charge and so I have learned the importance of taking responsibility. At school, I have formed a science club and invite speakers to come to talk to us once a month. Incidentally, Mr Ferguson, who is one of your research engineers, came to talk to us last month about developments in GPS systems, and we found his talk extremely informative.

I hope that you will be able to consider me for a post. I can be contacted by telephone or email at your earliest convenience.

Yours sincerely

Darren Fletcher

Work experience interviews

If you are lucky, you may then be called for an interview. Most of the advice given in Chapter 6, on university interviews, is also relevant to job interviews. Other points to remember are listed below.

- Do some research on the company in advance. Know about what they produce and how long they have been operating.
- Ensure that you can explain how your particular skills and qualities would be useful to them.
- Be clear about when you can start, how long you can work for, and whether there are particular periods when you cannot work, for example on the day your examination results are released.
- Wear smart clothes, a business suit if possible. Ensure that you have polished your shoes and don't wear too much jewellery.
- Introduce yourself, address the main interviewer by name, and offer your hand for a handshake at the start and again at the end.

How to use your work experience effectively

Undertaking work experience is a means to an end – to show the university selectors that you are a serious candidate. You will be expected to write about what you discovered about being an engineer in your personal statement, and to discuss it in more detail at your interview. It is useful to keep a diary of your experiences while you are there. Record what you did, saw and heard, and in particular conversations you had with engineers – not just technical things, but about their training and what they see as the main challenges and rewards in working in an engineering field. It is also a good idea to then do some research or reading on things that you encountered during your work placement.

ADAMS GRAMMAR SCHOOL
LIBRARY

3 | Choosing your course

Choosing universities and courses can be a bewildering experience because you will be confronted by an enormous number of options. This chapter covers the steps that you should take to narrow your search and to find the most appropriate courses for you.

What to consider

You are allowed five choices on the UCAS application. The basic factors to consider when choosing your degree course are:

- the engineering course you are looking for
- where you want to study
- the kind of university you are aiming for
- your academic ability.

You need to think seriously about your choice of universities, as the decisions you will take now may determine your future career options. At this stage, you may already have an idea of which universities you want to consider, based on the advice of friends and/or family, but you need to be as open-minded as possible. Make a list of between 10 and 20 universities in which you are interested; it's then important to reduce this to a much shorter list. Not only will the university be where you begin the next step in your education, it will also be your home for three or four years, so think carefully about the location, environment and accommodation options as well as the suitability of the course(s) on offer.

Here are some things to research and consider for each university.

- Get hold of the prospectuses and any departmental brochures for more details. Remember that university publications are there to attract applicants as well as to provide information, and may be selective about the information they provide, so read all of it bearing this in mind.
- Visit the websites of the universities you are considering. This is the best place to look for the most current information about a university. Another useful element to university websites is information on past and present students from a range of disciplines who give their views on student life at the institution. Some university websites

even have email links to current students who can answer any questions that you may have.

- Find out when the open days are and go to them if you possibly can. You will have a chance to look at the facilities, talk to current students and find out more about the course.

- The university is likely to be your home for three or four years, so think carefully about the location, environment and accommodation options.

- Discuss engineering and studying it as a subject with people you know who work as, or with, engineers; ask for their views on the reputations of different universities and courses. This may bring up some highly rated engineering institutions you may not have thought of.

- Investigate the grade requirements and be realistic about the grades you are expecting – your teachers at school or college will be able to advise you on this.

- Check that the course allows you to choose the particular options in which you are interested. If you are considering, for example, mechanical engineering but have a particular interest in aeronautics or automotive engineering, make sure that these options are available. You will not always know what each option actually covers by its title, so read the department's own prospectus carefully and address any unanswered questions by contacting the admissions tutors directly – contact details are usually on the departmental website.

- Think about whether you would like your course to include a placement with an engineering company. This might be for a few weeks, a term, or even a year. If this is something that interests you, find out who organises the placement – you or the university – and whether there is any funding to cover, for example, travelling costs or subsistence.

- Consider whether you want to spend some time abroad. Many engineering courses offer the option of a year abroad, studying at a partner university. If so, think about practical details such as language or visa requirements.

- Investigate how much practical or laboratory work is included in the course, and what are the practical engineering facilities. Find out whether the facilities include state-of-the-art machinery or testing equipment.

- Look at what IT facilities are offered. If you do not have your own laptop, will the university have facilities for you to manage without one of your own? Access to computing facilities can be very important when you are working on a dissertation. Find out whether there is wireless internet access in the study areas and/or accommodation.

- Ask about the reading lists, and whether the books are available in the library. Are you required to buy your own textbooks? If so, are second-hand copies available?

- Look up the specialties of the engineering course staff. Are they experts in the field of engineering in which you are particularly interested? Use the internet to find out what their experience is and what they have published, as this will give you a better indication of a department's strengths.

League tables

Newspapers often feature university rankings or league tables but there is no official ranking of universities or university courses in the UK, and so these tables are created using criteria selected by the newspapers themselves. There is a significant amount of variation between these tables, because each table will score the universities in a different way.

However, as long as you approach these rankings with caution, these tables can be a useful aid to the selection process, particularly if you look at how the rankings are assessed rather than simply looking at a university's position in the tables. There will be some criteria that you might regard as being important to you – graduate job prospects, for example – while you might not be so interested in the student to teacher ratios.

The list below shows the *Guardian* newspaper's ranking of the top 10 universities in the UK for 2013 (www.guardian.co.uk/education/universityguide, © Guardian News & Media Ltd 2012).

 1 Cambridge
 2 Oxford
 3 London School of Economics
 4 St Andrews
 5 Warwick
 6 University College London
 7= Durham
 7= Lancaster
 9 Bath
10 Exeter

As a potential engineer, you may want to investigate further, particularly as more than one of the universities in this list do not offer engineering courses.

The list below shows the *Guardian* 2013 rankings for general engineering courses (© Guardian News & Media Ltd 2012).

 1 Cambridge
 2 Imperial College
 3 Bournemouth
 4 Oxford
 5 Exeter
 6 Warwick

7 Leicester
8 Loughborough
9 Birmingham
10 Central Lancashire

The list below shows the *Guardian* 2013 rankings for civil engineering courses (© Guardian News & Media Ltd 2012).

1 University College London
2 Bath
3 Surrey
4 Loughborough
5 Dundee
6= Leeds
6= Sheffield
8 Heriot-Watt
9 West of Scotland
10 Bristol

These rankings include a number of areas of assessment, some of which may not be relevant to you. The *Guardian* rankings can be re-ordered on the website by clicking on the category that you think is most important. For example, the list below gives the ranking for civil engineering ordered by the entrance tariff of students being accepted onto the course (which is a good indication of the quality of the students, © Guardian News & Media Ltd 2012).

1 Imperial College
2 University College London
3 Bristol
4 Bath
5 Edinburgh
6 Sheffield
7 Southampton
8 Cardiff
9 Glasgow
10 Manchester

You might be interested in how the UK's universities are regarded on the global stage, particularly if you are an international student or you are planning on working abroad at some stage in your career. There are a number of world university rankings which you might find useful. But bear in mind that, like the UK university rankings, they are not in any way 'official' rankings and are based on criteria that the organisations compiling them see as being important.

One example is the world university rankings compiled by *Times Higher Education* (www.timeshighereducation.co.uk), which places Oxford second, Cambridge seventh, Imperial College eighth and University College London seventeenth in the world's top 20.

There are many other league tables and rankings, for example the one produced by *The Sunday Times* newspaper for UK universities, or by QS, which specialises in business education, for world rankings. No two rankings will produce the same results and so you need to use them as part of the process in making your decisions, not as the sole reason for a choice of university.

After completing your research, you should be able to narrow down your original list to the five choices for your UCAS form. Once you have done this, discuss the list with your teachers to see whether they think it includes sensible choices. They may ask you to think again about some of the choices.

Common areas of concern for teachers are:

- if all of the universities you have chosen require the same entrance grades, which makes choosing an insurance offer (see page 40) difficult
- that the grade requirements are too high (or too low) for the applicant's likely academic achievements
- that there is too much variation within the choice of courses to enable the applicant to write a coherent and focused personal statement (see Chapter 5).

Choosing the right course

Most universities offer a wide range of engineering courses, and it is important for you to investigate these thoroughly before making your choices. A particular university might list the following on the UCAS website:

- Aeronautical engineering
- Aeronautical engineering with a year abroad
- Biomedical engineering
- Biomedical engineering with a year abroad
- Chemical engineering
- Chemical engineering with a year abroad
- Chemical with nuclear engineering
- Civil engineering
- Civil engineering with a year abroad
- Electrical and electronic engineering
- Electrical and electronic engineering with a year abroad
- Electrical and electronic engineering with management
- Information systems engineering
- Materials science and engineering
- Mechanical engineering
- Mechanical engineering with a year abroad
- Structural engineering

A broad outline of general engineering courses can be found on page 9, but see the university website and prospectus for more details on specialisms. You will need to spend some time going through these.

When considering possible courses, read through all of the course content. Do not choose a course just because of its title. Courses with the same name at different universities can vary immensely in their content, and within the courses themselves the likelihood is that you will have a range of options to choose from once you start your course. This is also important if you are interviewed (see Chapter 6) because you may be asked to justify your choice. Being able to discuss the course structure in detail will be an important factor in convincing the interviewer that you are a serious applicant.

Similar-sounding courses also do not always have the same entrance requirements (examination results and preferred A level subjects). Examination results are specified as either grade requirements (for example AAB) or tariff points (for example 300 – see Chapter 11). Unless you are applying post-results (as a mature applicant or during your gap year), your referee will be asked to predict the grades that you are expected to achieve in your examinations. You should find out in advance what he or she is going to predict, because this will determine your choice of universities and courses. For example, if you apply for five university courses that require AAB but your A level predictions are BBB, there will be a high chance of being rejected by all of your choices. You will then have to try to find alternatives through the UCAS Extra scheme, or through Clearing (see Chapter 8). Similarly, if you are predicted to achieve A*AA, you are probably aiming too low if all of the courses you are applying for require CCC at A level.

As a rough guide, if you are predicted, say, ABB, it would be risky to choose a course that requires AAB. It would be safer to choose three or four that require ABB, and one or two that require BBB. This means that you not only have a good chance of getting a number of offers, but it also gives you options if you do not quite meet the grade requirements (see Chapter 8).

Placements and overseas study

Studying abroad and/or completing a work placement could also be factors that affect your degree selection. It is possible to study engineering in many countries as part of a degree based at a British university. Not all of these courses send you off for a full year, though: there are schemes that last for only one term or semester. You do not need to be a linguist either, as it is always possible to study overseas in an English-speaking location such as North America, South Africa, Australia or Malaysia.

The availability of student exchanges has increased through pro-grammes such as Erasmus, which encourage universities to provide international opportunities where practical – particularly in Europe. The popularity of overseas study has encouraged some universities to develop special exchange relationships with universities further afield.

Academic and career-related factors

Academic ability

It is important to be honest about what you think you will achieve in your A levels or equivalent because, for most, this is the deciding factor for selection. The best way to get a strong sense of your predicted results is to speak to your teachers.

Remember, be realistic; you may think that you can do much better than your teachers' predictions or than your AS results indicate, but the pre-dicted grades and previous results will go on your UCAS application form, and so it is important to ensure that the courses you apply for are consistent with your likely results. If you do much better than expected, you can always 'upgrade' using the UCAS Adjustment scheme (see page 87). Check also whether the universities are likely to make a grade or tariff points offer. If the grade requirement is, for example, AAB, don't assume that a combination of grades that gives you the same tariff points (340, achieved by gaining A*BB) would satisfy the university's requirements.

For more details about UCAS and filling in your application, see *How to Complete Your UCAS Application: 2014 entry* (Trotman Publishing, 2013).

Educational facilities

Take a look at the facilities the university has to offer. Here is a checklist of what to look out for:

- access to lecturers if you need help
- computer facilities
- course materials
- laboratory provision
- lecture theatres
- library facilities
- multimedia facilities
- study facilities.

Quality of teaching

The Higher Education Funding Council for England, the Higher Education Funding Council for Wales, the Scottish Funding Council and the Department for Education and Learning of Northern Ireland assess the level of teaching across the UK. Their findings are publicly available – see www.hefce.ac.uk, www.hefcw.ac.uk, www.sfc.ac.uk and www.delni.gov.uk. League tables (see page 23) normally incorporate these into their rankings.

Type of institution

There are three types of institution from which you can obtain a degree:

- 'old' universities
- 'new' universities
- higher education colleges.

The 'old' universities

These are traditionally seen as the more academic universities (Oxford and Cambridge to name a couple), usually with higher admission requirements, and with a strong emphasis on research.

The 'new' universities

Pre-1992 these were polytechnics, institutes or colleges, for example Kingston, Central Lancashire and Westminster. These tended to focus more on vocational courses with less emphasis (or none at all) on research. There are a number of excellent engineering degree courses at new universities that are very well regarded and highly competitive to get into, and they are often more flexible in terms of sandwich courses, work placements or links with industry.

Colleges of higher education

These are specialist institutions that have links with universities. The university awards the degree and can deliver part of the course, along with the institution. Many colleges also offer pathway programmes, such as Access or foundation courses for students who do not have the necessary academic qualifications for direct entry to a university.

Non-academic considerations

Finances

Finance is an important factor to consider, as you will need to juggle a lot of outgoings when you go to university. You will need to take into account:

- accommodation costs
- availability of part-time work in the area to earn some extra money
- living costs, such as food
- travel from your accommodation to the university during term time
- travel from your home to and from the university for holidays
- proximity to your home, family and friends – will it cost you a lot of money to visit friends or to go home?

Accommodation

Accommodation can vary wildly between institutions so you will need to think about where you would feel most comfortable. Do you want to live in halls of residence with other students, or independently (or with friends) in rented houses or flats? Do you want to be near your lectures or are you happy to live further away from the university?

Universities all have accommodation offices that provide help or information for students who do not want to, or are unable to, live in university-provided accommodation. Most universities offer arranged accommodation for first-year students in halls of residence, which may either be owned by the university or be shared with other institutions, but often students are expected to find their own accommodation in subsequent years.

Entertainment

You will be spending the next few years in a new place so you will need to have a look at the entertainment facilities it has to offer both within and outside the university. Are your particular interests or hobbies catered for? If you're a keen sports enthusiast, have a look at the facilities on offer and the sorts of clubs and teams you can join.

Site and size

- Campus university outside a town or city?
- Campus within a town or city?
- University buildings at various locations within a town or city?
- Large or small?

While some students have a clear picture of where they want to study, others are fairly geographically mobile, preferring instead to concentrate on choosing the right degree course and see where they end up. But university life is not going to be solely about academic study. It is truly a growing experience – educationally, socially and culturally – and so you need to do your research and think carefully to ensure that you choose the best university and course for you.

4 | Completing your UCAS application

This chapter is designed to help you complete your UCAS application. Further advice on filling in your application is given in *How to Complete Your UCAS Application*, which is updated every year.

The UCAS application

The UCAS application is completed using Apply, the online application system on the UCAS website. There are five sections to complete.

1. **Personal information:** name, contact details, home address and nationality (for fee purposes – see Chapter 9).
2. **Your choices of university and course:** you have up to five choices of university or courses. This is entered by using codes for the university and the course. You need to take great care in ensuring that this is accurate. You will also be able to specify the year of entry (are you planning on a gap year?) and whether you want to live at home. Some universities, such as Oxford, Cambridge and Durham, operate a college system so you also have to choose which college you wish to be associated with.
3. **Education:** past examination results, details of your previous and current schools and colleges, and future examinations. This section requires particular care, and you will need to discuss this with your school or college to ensure that, for example, AS unit results are correctly entered.
4. **Employment:** have you been in full-time employment?
5. **Personal statement:** see Chapter 5.

When you have completed the application, you save it and mark it as complete. You then send it to your referee via the UCAS website. He or she will then complete the reference and, if applicable, add predicted grades or scores. If you are applying as a private candidate, you will add the reference directly onto the form yourself (see Chapter 7).

University engineering departments are looking for motivated, well-qualified individuals, and so they are keen to provide as much encouragement and practical advice as possible. If you look hard enough, you will find lots of information from the universities that will help you with your application. As an example, see the excerpts from the admissions advice on the Bristol University website for MEng Engineering Mathematics applicants in the box below.

Advice on the UCAS application process from Bristol University

All applicants are contacted within four weeks of receipt of the application, to establish contact and inform them of the process to be followed. Applications that are received on time (in accordance with the deadlines of the UCAS application cycle) are guaranteed equal consideration. All applications are considered on an equal basis, and are not segregated by the type of educational institution attended.

All applications are allocated scores on the academic record and the personal statement/reference.

The weighting is as follows:

- academic score: 80%
- personal statement/reference score: 20%

Applicants whom we expect to make an offer to are invited to attend one of the Departmental Visit/UCAS Days, normally from November to March. The visit is to allow students to find out more about the University and the content of our programmes. The visit also allows us to personalise offers as appropriate. As part of the visit each applicant is offered a 20–30-minute one-on-one session with a member of academic staff. Details of the offer are confirmed through UCAS.

Although there are other opportunities to visit the department, such as University Open Days, if a candidate is invited to attend an Admissions Day then they are expected to attend even if they have attended one of these other University events. This is because the Admissions Day is specifically tailored to prospective students, as well as giving the admissions team an opportunity to clarify issues that may not be clear from the application forms and to help decide on the details of any offer to be made. Allowance is made, however, for a candidate who cannot make an Admissions Day due to any exceptional circumstance; if this is the case then the applicant should inform the Admissions Team as soon as possible.

Personal statement criteria

We use the following criteria for assessing the personal statement:

- additional academic preparation and achievements
- competitions, other mathematical or electrical and electronic engineering-related activity

- personal factors such as relevant work experience, being given a level of responsibility (i.e. mentoring, head girl or boy, etc.)
- overall well-written English, expression and construction of the personal statement.

Overall, the statement should demonstrate a genuine interest in the chosen programme and basic knowledge of the subject, highlighting relevant skills in mathematics and problem solving. It should also give evidence of strong study skills, responsibility, leadership and team working, commitment and achievement, both in academic and extracurricular activities. Any relevant work experience or a Year in Industry placement should be highlighted along with any relevant reading/research beyond the A level course syllabus. We are also interested in evidence of organisation, self-motivation, and the ability to balance different activities.

Reprinted with kind permission of Bristol University, www.bris.ac.uk

Suggested timescale

Use the timescale below to help you plan your application.

Year 12

In year 12, during your first year of A levels or IB, you should start to think seriously about what type of engineering course you want to follow. Talk to as many people as possible – your teachers, family and careers advisers. Don't just focus on what area of engineering interests you most, but also on whether you want a three-year BEng course or a four-year MEng course, whether you want a campus university or one in the centre of a city, close to home or in another part of the country.

Your next step should be to find out when the universities that interest you have open days and arrange to visit them. After this, you ought to be in a position to make up a shortlist of courses and universities, ready for your application. You can start to order prospectuses from the universities, or download the PDF versions from the university websites. Remember to make a note of the grade requirements for your chosen universities.

In August, refine your choices in the light of your AS results or predicted examination results.

Year 13

In September of year 13, you can submit your UCAS application. The deadline for applications is 15 January, but I recommend that you apply as early as possible. If you are applying to Oxford or Cambridge universities, your application has to be submitted by 15 October. Some universities will want to interview you, and this can happen from November onwards. If you are required to sit entrance tests, you may be asked to do this in the first week of November.

You should start to hear back from the universities from January onwards, although some universities might get back to you earlier than this. You can keep up to date with the status of your applications using the online UCAS Track facility.

If you are unlucky enough to receive rejections from all of your choices, or you decide to withdraw from your choices, you can then use the UCAS Extra scheme in March to apply to other universities.

Once you have received responses from all five universities (or offers through UCAS Extra), you will be given a deadline by UCAS by which time you have to choose one university as your firm acceptance, and a second insurance offer, normally one that requires lower grades. Once you have accepted your first choice university, you will be sent information about accommodation and fees and other practical information directly from the universities.

You sit your examinations in the summer, and receive your results in July or August:

- A level results are published in the third week of August
- Scottish Higher results are released in the first week of August
- IB results come out in the first week of July.

When the exam results are published, UCAS will get in touch and tell you whether your chosen universities have confirmed your conditional offers. Do not be too disappointed if you have not got into your chosen institution; just get in touch with your school/college or careers office and wait until Clearing begins in mid-August, when all remaining places are filled. You will be sent instructions on Clearing automatically, but it is up to you to get hold of the published lists of available places and to contact the universities directly.

If you have done better than expected, you can use the Adjustment system to look for universities that require higher grades. For 2013 entry, the government-imposed quota on places for home/EU students has been waived for students achieving ABB (or the equivalent in IB or Scottish Highers). In other words, if you achieve ABB, a university that has reached its maximum number of students for any particular course is still able to accept more ABB students if it chooses to do so.

Entrance examinations

As competition for places is so fierce, some universities ask applicants to sit entrance examinations as part of the application process.

Cambridge University

If you are applying to Cambridge University you will have to sit an extra entrance examination, the Thinking Skills Assessment (TSA).

The information below is taken from the specimen papers available on the Admissions Testing Service website (www.admissionstestingservice.org).

- This test is taken at the interview.
- It consists of 50 questions to be completed in 90 minutes.
- Details can be found at the website listed above.

The TSA is available as an online or paper-based test. The college to which you are applying will specify which version you will take.

Sample test questions for the Cambridge TSA

School examination results in England this year reinforce the trend in improving pass rates. There is, however, no other evidence of improvements in school-leavers' abilities – such as the data coming from employers or universities. One can reasonably conclude, therefore, that teachers are simply succeeding in coaching their pupils better for examinations than in previous years.

Which one of the following is an underlying assumption of the above argument?

A   School examination results are a reliable indicator of pupils' abilities.
B   The level of difficulty of examinations has not been falling.
C   Employers' expectations of school-leavers are unrealistic.
D   Teachers in previous years did not attempt to coach pupils for examinations.
E   Abilities of school pupils vary from year to year.

Ever since Uranus was discovered in 1781, astronomers have thought there might be more planets to be discovered in the Solar System. Because of small deviations in the orbits of Uranus

---

and Neptune – deviations which would occur if another planet existed – some astronomers think there must be an undiscovered planet – Planet X. But the search for Planet X is futile, because these deviations would occur if the orbits had been wrongly predicted. Since Uranus and Neptune take many decades to circle the sun, astronomers must rely on old data in order to calculate their orbits. If this data is inaccurate, the calculated orbits are wrong. If the calculated orbits are wrong, Uranus and Neptune will deviate from them even if there is no Planet X.

Which of the following is the best statement of the flaw in the argument above?

A From the fact that the old data is inaccurate, it cannot be inferred that the calculated orbits are wrong.

B From the fact that the data about the orbits is old it cannot be inferred that it is inaccurate.

C From the fact that deviations occur which would occur if Planet X existed, it cannot be inferred that Planet X exists.

D From the fact that the calculated orbits are wrong, it cannot be inferred that Uranus and Neptune will deviate from them.

E From the fact that Planet X has not been discovered, it cannot be inferred that the search for it is futile.

The roller coaster at Blue Top Towers Park runs continuously from 10a.m. to 6p.m. during the week and from 9a.m. to 7p.m. at weekends.

Each ride lasts for 3 minutes.

It can take up to 5 minutes to unload and reload between rides at busy periods, but even when the park is quiet there is a 2-minute gap between the end of one ride and the beginning of the next.

What is the maximum number of rides there can be in one day?

A 60
B 75
C 96
D 120
E 200

From the specimen papers available on the Admissions Testing Service website (www.admissionstestingservice.org). Reprinted by permission of the University of Cambridge Local Examinations Syndicate.

Answers are: B, B, D

Oxford University

Engineering applicants for Oxford University have to sit the Physics Aptitude Test (PAT). The test is sat at your school or college in the first week of November. You have to register for the test by 15 October.

The paper is two hours long and is divided into two sections: Section A, Mathematics for Physics; and Section B, Physics.

Section B comprises multiple-choice answers and written answers. A typical question might involve being given the electric current recorded when a box containing electrical components with three terminals is connected in different ways to a power supply. You would have to deduce what the components are and the values of their electrical resistance from the data.

Other universities

Cardiff University, Kingston University, Ulster University and Liverpool John Moores University may ask some candidates for engineering courses to sit a separate entrance test. (In the course requirements information on the UCAS website, this is listed as 'IOT', which means 'institution's own test'.) Not all candidates are asked to do the test, and you will be given information about whether you need to sit the test, and its format, when you apply. The tests are used as one piece of evidence in assessing candidates, alongside many other criteria such as grades achieved, predicted grades, the personal statement and references.

Taking a gap year: deferred entry

Many students take a gap year between their final school or college examinations and the start of their university course. Universities are nearly always happy with this as students who take a year away from studies are often more motivated and mature when they start their degree studies. But in terms of the application, a gap year will only enhance your chances of getting a place if you use the year productively.

There are two application routes for students taking a gap year.

- You can apply for deferred entry; that is, you apply in the final year of the A level course for entry a year later. So, if you are sitting A levels in June 2013 you would apply for entry in September/October 2014, not 2013.
- Alternatively, you can apply at the start of the gap year, once your A level results are known.

There are advantages to both routes, depending on your plans and A level grades.

Advantages of deferred entry

- Once you have satisfied your offer, you will know where you will be studying in a year's time, and so you can make firm plans about what you will do during the year.
- You can plan to be overseas, either travelling or on work or voluntary placements, without worrying about having to return for university interviews.
- You have a second chance to apply to universities during the gap year if your initial application is unsuccessful.

Advantages of applying during the gap year

- You have more time to decide which field of engineering really interests you.
- You will already know your results so you can focus your application on those universities for which you have already achieved the necessary grades or scores.
- If your predicted grades are not high, but you feel confident of doing better than your school or college expects, you can avoid the possibility of being rejected on the basis of your predictions rather than actual ability.

If you are planning on taking a gap year, you must plan it carefully so that you will gain something from it. This could be life or work experience, maturity, a chance to extend your studies into new areas, independence or money to fund your university studies. A year spent resting and playing computer games, however attractive that may be after all your hard work at school, is not going to convince the universities that you will be a stronger candidate as a result.

Here is an excerpt from a personal statement about taking a gap year:

> 'I am taking a gap year in order to gain more maturity and experience.'

Such a statement is not going to convince the admissions tutors that you have made constructive plans for your gap year, nor is it likely to help you develop or bring new skills and ideas onto their course.

A better statement might be:

> 'During my gap year, I have arranged a placement with a local company that manufactures electric motors. This will be useful because it will give me an insight into the whole process of commercial production as well as giving me a chance to learn more about the practical uses of mechanical and electrical engineering. As an engineer, you have to be aware of issues such as cost-

effectiveness, safety and environmental issues as well as the technical side. I will also work part time in a local petrol station to earn some money for my travels. This will help me to improve my communication skills. In February I have planned a trip to Thailand, Vietnam and Cambodia. I will then go to Australia for two months to work with my uncle who is an architect, and I hope to learn more about the process of turning designs into real buildings.'

This is much more impressive because the candidate has linked what she will do in her gap year to her future degree course (electrical engineering), and it is clear that she has thought carefully about what she will do during the year.

A piece of advice: phrases such as 'I have arranged to . . .' are much more convincing than 'I hope to . . .' when discussing your gap-year plans.

Gap-year plans

It is always a good idea to check with your chosen universities that a gap year is acceptable to them before committing yourself. There is likely to be information on their websites addressing this. If there is none, you can email the admissions staff to ask them. This is particularly important if you are taking a gap year for reasons other than wanting to take a year between school studies and the degree course to gain experience in engineering.

Some of the other reasons for taking a gap year are:

- to work towards extra qualifications because you need to strengthen your application, or because you wish to change direction (for example, if you had studied mathematics up to AS level only, you will be doing an evening class in A2 mathematics alongside your other projects)
- you started another course (such as a degree course in another subject) and then realised that it is not right for you, so you have withdrawn from it
- you have been working, and you now want to return to studying
- you may have had an illness or other issues that required you to take a break from studying.

Replies from the universities

After your application has been assessed by the university, you will receive a response. You can also follow the progress of your application using the online Track facility on the UCAS website. You will receive one of three possible responses from each university:

- conditional offer
- unconditional offer
- rejection.

If you receive a conditional offer, you will be told what you need to achieve in your A levels. This could be in grade terms, for example AAB (and the university might specify a particular grade in a particular subject – AAB, with an A in mathematics), or in UCAS tariff points (300 points from three A levels – see Chapter 11). Unconditional offers can be given to students who have already sat their A levels, such as gap-year students applying post-results. Rejection means that you have been unsuccessful in your application to that university.

Once you have received responses from all five universities, you will need to make your choice of the university offer you wish to accept. This is called your firm choice. You can also choose an insurance offer, effectively a second choice with a lower grade requirement. UCAS will give you a deadline of about a month from the date that you received your fifth response to make this decision.

If you receive five rejections, or if you reject all of the offers you have received, then you can enter the UCAS Extra scheme, through which you can make additional choices. See page 34 for more on Extra.

ADAMS GRAMMAR SCHOOL
LIBRARY

5 | The personal statement

A rguably, the most important part of your UCAS application is the personal statement. It is also the one part of the form where you have complete freedom to decide how you wish to demonstrate your suitability for the course to the selectors. You have 4,000 characters (47 lines) to convince your five chosen universities that:

- you have good reasons for studying engineering
- you have researched your future career thoroughly
- you have appropriate personal and academic qualities to become a successful engineer
- you will be able to contribute something to the department and to the university.

Who will read your personal statement?

Before you can write a personal statement you have to think carefully about your choice of courses. This is because each admissions tutor will read the personal statement with his or her own course in mind, and he or she will expect what you write to be consistent with the course. For this reason, make sure that the five courses you choose are closely linked in terms of course content and outcome. If you are applying for a civil engineering course, the selector will expect to read about your interest in civil engineering, books related to the subject that you have read, and relevant work experience. Similarly, an admissions tutor for electronic engineering will expect the personal statement to address this subject. Clearly, you cannot convince both that you are serious about their courses in one personal statement.

> ### Advice from an admissions tutor
>
> Your personal statement is your chance to tell me what makes you special. I can already see your academic profile (past and predicted), so this is your opportunity to tell me how you're going to contribute to the Cardiff academic and social community. Is there something that makes you unique and you think we might value? Tell me about

it and how you think this is relevant to studying engineering. Lots of students talk about how well rounded they are, and in the eyes of many admissions tutors, this is important. But once in a while I would like to read about an applicant who is truly special and unique. Have you done well in the face of adversity? Have you spent time in another culture? A leader? An athlete? How have these experiences made you better, and how will your skills help you to succeed and stand out amongst a group of other high-achieving peers? If you think it is relevant, tell me about it. Don't have anything like this to write about? That's OK too – maybe instead you can write about what challenges you expect to face in the transition to university and how you will overcome them.

Barry Sullivan, Head of Admissions, Cardiff School of Engineering, Cardiff University

Joint honours courses

Personal statements for joint honours courses are usually read by selectors from both of the departments to which you are applying. If you want to apply for a joint honours engineering and management course, someone from the engineering faculty will expect to read about engineering while their colleagues from the management department will want to read about management. This is fine if you apply to five similar courses, but if you apply for, say, three engineering with management and two single honours engineering courses you will find it difficult to satisfy the selectors from the two different types of course. Discuss your course choices with your careers adviser to assess how best to present these choices in your personal statement.

Applying for different courses at the same university

You can apply for more than one course at a particular university; you do not have to choose five different universities. But applying for two courses at the same university does not necessarily increase your chances of studying there. Take the case of a student who is desperate to study at a particular university, perhaps because she has friends there or she likes the city. She decides to apply for both the civil engineering and biomedical engineering courses. The admissions tutor for civil engineering will look at her application for the civil engineering course, and the admissions tutor for biomedical engineering will look at the application for this course.

Our applicant's main interest is civil engineering, so her personal statement emphasises this, but it also devotes one paragraph to her interest in biomedical issues. The civil engineering admissions tutor reading the personal statement will judge it on how it addresses this course, so he or she might not be fully convinced that the student is serious because the personal statement will not focus enough on the reasons for the choice of civil engineering, and what the candidate has done to investigate it (reading, work experience, etc.). Similarly, biomedical engineering is a very specialist area, and the admissions tutor for this course will expect to read a personal statement that focuses on this, and he or she is not going to be very interested in reading about bridges and roads.

So, by trying to give herself a better chance of getting to this university, the applicant is actually reducing her chances. There are some instances where it is possible to apply for two separate courses at the same university, if they are very similar, but it would be advisable to discuss this with the university admissions department before doing so. So, when writing the personal statement, try to imagine how it will come across to each of the departments to which you are applying. Do not try to write something too general in order to allow yourself the luxury of applying to a wider range of courses.

Advice from an admissions tutor

From a personal statement, we are looking for a well-rounded but focused and committed individual. Therefore, an indication that they can get their hands dirty (metaphorically speaking) over a long-term technical project is highly desirable. What we are not interested in are flowery quotes about the applicant wanting to solve the world's problems (often encouraged by parents and teachers). Our alarm bells also start ringing when an applicant has too many non-academic commitments, but equally no outside interests.

Dr Stepan Lucyszyn, Undergraduate Admissions Tutor for the Department of Electrical and Electronic Engineering (EEE), Imperial College London

---

The structure of the personal statement

What is a perfect personal statement? Of course, there is no such thing. The key to writing a personal statement is to think about the word 'personal' – it is about you and so it has to reflect your strengths, achievements, qualities, research and ambitions. Having said that, there are some elements that are important in creating a successful personal statement:

- reasons for your choice of course
- what you have done to investigate the course and the profession
- what unique qualities and achievements you have
- other things that may affect your application, such as gap-year plans.

Reasons for your choice of course

These could include:

- what first got you thinking about engineering, for example watching the news about a new engineering project, an article in a newspaper about new developments in the mobile phone industry, or personal experience such as work experience – this could date back many years, for example how you liked taking things apart and reassembling them when you were very young
- things you have studied at school, for example a topic in physics or chemistry that particularly interested you
- how your particular interests and qualities make engineering a suitable career.

What you have done to investigate engineering

This could include:

- books, articles, magazines or websites that you have read
- work experience (see Chapter 2)
- talks or lectures
- the relevance to engineering of things you have studied at school.

Your qualities or achievements

These could include:

- academic achievements, for example Mathematics Challenge
- extracurricular activities and accomplishments
- responsibilities, for example sports captain, head of house, chairman of a club or society
- evidence of teamwork, for example the school orchestra, Duke of Edinburgh expeditions, part-time jobs
- hobbies.

Other information relevant to the application

This could include:

- gap-year plans
- if you are an international student, why you want to study in the UK

- what qualities or experiences you could offer to the university or the course.

A sample personal statement

Character count (with spaces): 1,746

I first became interested in engineering during my AS physics classes [1]. As a child I had always enjoyed taking things apart, although I was not always able to put them back together again.

To further investigate engineering, I spent a week at a local architecture practice, looking at how they worked with a structural engineer to ensure that their designs were practical. I also visited a construction project as part of my school's work experience programme, and I was fascinated to see how things I had read about and studied were used in real life [2]. I have also read as much as I can about engineering, including *A Short History of Engineering Materials* by John Cameron [3]. I have enjoyed going to public lectures on engineering, and talking to engineers, who have given me a much better idea about a career as an engineer [4].

Alongside physics, I am studying mathematics and history of art. Mathematics is an important tool for engineers [5], as well as teaching me to think in a logical way. History of art is an analytical subject, and it puts architecture within a social and political context. It also involves looking at the use of materials, and how architecture and sculpture were able to develop as new materials were introduced [6].

I enjoy sport and music. I am captain of my school football team and so have had to develop leadership and communication skills as well as physical fitness. I play the guitar in a band, and the cello in the school orchestra, which help me with my manual dexterity and teamwork. Outside of school, I enjoy cooking and cycling. I am a member of my local cycling club and compete most weekends.

I believe that my combination of A levels and my research into engineering as a career make engineering an ideal choice for me.

Points raised by this personal statement

An admissions tutor who read this sample personal statement made the following points.

General

While it is clear that the candidate has done some research, there is very little detail in the statement – it is very general – and so I do not really get a clear picture of the depth of knowledge the candidate has about engineering, or about his/her particular areas of interest. It is also, to be honest, a little on the bland side and also a bit frustrating – a lot of sentences which should lead to something that will interest me end without giving me any information.

Specific points (the numbers refer to the relevant passages in the statement)

1. It would have been nice if he/she could have given an example – perhaps it was electricity, or the behaviour of materials, or some problems involving forces?
2. This should have been the most interesting part of the statement. The candidate could have told me about the links between his/her studies and the work experience. This will tell me that the student has gained something from the work experience, and that he/she is thinking about engineering rather than just doing work experience to look good on the application form.
3. I am always encouraged when students read around the subject, but what I would like to know is, again, some detail. How do the ideas in the book link to A level study and the real world?
4. This would have been an ideal opportunity for the candidate to show me that he/she has been really thinking hard about his/her future career and about whether he/she has the right qualities to be a successful engineer.
5. Give an example.
6. Not many applicants for engineering study history of art, so this immediately makes him/her stand out. And I don't know much about history of art, so an example here would be interesting for me to learn about – I'm sure it would make me want to learn more by meeting the candidate.

A revised (and much better) version of the personal statement, based on the above advice, is now given.

Revised sample personal statement

Character count (with spaces): 3,064

As a child I had always enjoyed taking things apart, although I was not always able to put them back together again. I first became seriously interested in engineering during my AS physics classes when we looked at the properties of solid materials, and I began

---

to understand why, for example, the development of reinforced concrete revolutionised the construction industry.

To further investigate engineering, I spent a week at a local architecture practice, looking at how they worked with a structural engineer to ensure that their designs were practical. I also visited a construction project as part of my school's work experience programme, and I was fascinated to see how things I had read about and studied were used in real life. The engineers explained that the concrete girders used to hang the curtain walls of the office block had to be strengthened along their top surfaces because in a cantilever, the tensile forces are at the top and concrete is weaker in tension than it is in compression. I have also read as much as I can about engineering, including 'A Short History of Engineering Materials' by John Cameron, and I was fascinated about how the use of cast iron in early 20th-century America enabled architects and engineers to build the prototypes to today's skyscrapers. I have enjoyed going to public lectures on engineering, and talking to engineers, who have given me a much better idea about a career as an engineer. In particular, I began to understand that an engineer needs to be able to analyse information quickly and to be able to solve problems. My aim is to study structural engineering and then to work alongside architects in the creation of exciting new buildings.

Alongside physics, I am studying mathematics and history of art. Mathematics is an important tool for engineers because the starting point of any engineering project is an analysis of its feasibility. The use of integration to find a centre of mass, for example, can help with the design of an asymmetric building. History of art is an analytical subject, and puts architecture within a social and political context. It also involves looking at the use of materials, and how architecture and sculpture were able to develop as new materials were introduced. The transition from the small, squat Romanesque churches to tall and graceful gothic cathedrals in Europe was due to the invention of the flying buttresses, which, in turn, were only effective when tensile forces were reduced by the addition of heavy statues or decorative stone elements.

I enjoy sport and music. I am captain of my school football team and so have had to develop leadership and communication skills as well as physical fitness. I play the guitar in a band, and the cello in the school orchestra, which help me with my manual dexterity and teamwork. Outside of school, I enjoy cooking and cycling. I am a member of my local cycling club and compete most weekends.

I believe that my combination of A levels and my research into engineering as a career make engineering an ideal choice for me.

Adding the extra information requested by this admissions tutor would add detail, make it more interesting for him to read (so he is more likely to want to meet the student), demonstrate that the student is interested enough in the subject to be thinking about links between his studies and what he has experienced, and bring it up to the required length.

> ### Advice from an admissions tutor
>
> Apart from good predicted A level and English examination results, we are looking for signs that the applicant has the bandwidth to comfortably attain his or her academic goals and to also enjoy other pursuits; for example the ability to master another language, musical instrument, sport or hobby, and take them to ever greater levels of achievement.
>
> Stepan Lucyszyn, Undergraduate Admissions Tutor for the Department of Electrical and Electronic Engineering (EEE), Imperial College London

Linking your interests and experiences

In your personal statement, try to avoid creating what amounts to a list of things you have read, studied or experienced. It is better to make connections between these in order to demonstrate that you have thought carefully about what is required to be a successful engineer:

- how your A level studies are related to things you will study at degree level
- how something you observed during work experience stimulated further reading
- how skills that you gained from extracurricular activities, such as communication or leadership, are useful for potential engineers.

You could link:

- an article you read about the increasing storage capacity of computer memory with something you studied about semiconductors
- the design of a new building with your study of forces in physics
- the need for engineers to be good communicators with your role as your class representative at school
- the follow-up research you did on wind turbines with an on-site visit on a school trip
- a news story on a new aircraft design with an article in the *New Scientist* about composite materials.

How to get started on the personal statement

A good strategy is to start by making lists of anything that you think is relevant to your application. Then begin to organise them into sections. Your personal statement could include some of the following points.

I first became interested in engineering because . . .

- I read an article in the newspaper about . . .
- I read the book '. . .'
- I saw a piece on the news about . . .
- my work experience
- my father's job
- of something I have enjoyed studying at school.

I have investigated engineering by . . .

- reading books
- reading the *New Scientist*
- reading the Royal Academy of Engineering website
- work experience
- going to a public lecture at a university
- discussing engineering with an engineer
- downloading a podcast of a university lecture on iTunes U.

From my work experience I learned . . .

- that the qualities necessary to become a successful engineer are . . .
- how the theory I study at A level is applied practically
- the importance of communication skills/accuracy/leadership . . .

Other points to include:

- a particular A level topic is useful because . . .
- my part-time job is useful because . . .
- my role as rugby captain has taught me . . .
- being leader of the school orchestra has taught me . . . (or hockey, or lead in the school play, or . . .)
- during my gap year I will be . . .
- I was awarded first prize for . . .

Only when you have the ideas listed should you start to write full sentences and to link the points. On no account should your first steps towards writing a personal statement be to:

- plan how you are going to say all you want in exactly 47 lines
- write down your ideas in perfectly formed sentences, suitable for the final version
- download sample personal statements from the internet and try to adapt them.

Language

It is important that you use succinct language in your personal statement and make every word count. Remember that you are limited on the number of characters you may use so it is important not to use up this vital space with superfluous language. Keep it as simple and clear as you can, rather than using overcomplicated language in an effort to impress.

For example:

> *'I was privileged to be able to undertake an internship with a well-known engineering company where I was able to see the benefit of having the ability to be confident with information technology'* – approximately 200 characters.

Could be rewritten as:

> *'My three weeks' work placement at Rolls-Royce showed me the importance of being proficient in using spreadsheets'* – approximately 110 characters.

Similarly:

> *'I was honoured to be chosen to play the lead role in my most recent school drama production, and interacting with the producer and the rest of the cast involved a significant degree of communication and teamwork'* – approximately 210 characters.

Could be rewritten as:

> *'Performing as the lead in my school play taught me to work and communicate effectively with others'* – approximately 100 characters.

Phrases to avoid

- 'It was an honour to . . .'
- 'I was privileged to . . .'
- 'From an early age . . .'
- 'For as long as I can remember, I have dreamt of . . .'

Sample personal statements

These statements were written by students applying for engineering courses.

Please remember that these are personal statements; that is, they reflect the experiences and ambitions of the students who wrote them – so **do not attempt to copy them or to adapt them for your own use**.

Personal statement 1

Character count (with spaces): 3,726

I come to read engineering from an unusual position. Along with A level chemistry, maths, further maths and ancient history, I studied design and technology: resistant materials to AS level. It was in studying design that I became convinced that what I wanted to study further was engineering. I therefore decided to use my gap year to study A level physics, which I am enjoying very much, particularly because it connects so many of the topics I have already studied.

Design introduced me to the properties of materials, and how these properties affect their applications in building and manufacture. Learning about carbon fibre and its uses in Formula 1 cars was particularly interesting. Chemistry enabled me to understand the composition of these materials and their resultant properties such as the lubricating properties of graphite created by the layers of carbon atoms. I have particularly enjoyed the mechanics modules of my maths courses, and look forward to further developing the mathematical models I have studied.

To get more of an insight into engineering as a degree I went on a Headstart course last summer at the University of Surrey. I enjoyed the whole experience, particularly the sessions focusing on the manufacture, properties, uses and limitations of reinforced concrete, where I was able to draw on my knowledge of moments from my mechanics modules and tensile and compressive forces from design. These gave me an idea about what being a structural engineer involves, and the problems they have to deal with. One of these in particular is that, due to the imperfections in the aggregate, concrete can fail in unexpected ways.

Further to this I worked at Bespak, a company manufacturing complex medical devices, including respirators and dose counters. One of the main reasons I decided on engineering was this experience. I was given two assignments to improve their current products; one to find an alternative mechanism to allow a tracheotomy device to work in an MRI scanner and the other to design the mechanism for a pocket dose counter. Although I did not find a definitive solution to these problems, I produced designs and ideas that were put into use, including a plastic spring for the tracheotomy device, something the company had not thought of before. I really enjoyed the entire experience; particularly being part of a problem-solving team. I also did some work experience with Palm Paper, which has recently set up the largest paper processing plant in Europe outside King's Lynn, which was fascinating, seeing this huge plant being set up, and manufacturing on such an enormous scale.

To further my knowledge of science and engineering I am now subscribing to 'New Scientist' and also I am going to lectures at the Royal Society. One of my great loves is ancient history and as an engineer I was stunned by the achievements of the ancient Greeks on a recent tour of the ancient sites. Having read 'Structures' by J.E. Gordon, I began to really appreciate how impressive some of these sites were.

I enjoy classical music and play the double bass with the school orchestra. It is a really rewarding experience when the whole piece comes together and a great team exercise as it relies on everyone to play their part right. I also have recently been stage manager for a school play which required a lot of organisation and leadership to make sure everyone was in the right place at the right time with their particular props. I have greatly enjoyed playing rugby for a school team for which I was made captain and running the local 10k marathon, which I have done three times in aid of the local hospice. Lastly, I am an avid reader, enjoying a complete cross-section of styles and subjects.

Personal statement 2

Character count (with spaces): 3,712

I have admired the power of science ever since my physics teacher taught me the theories and laws of physics. Why does Newton's law of gravitation work? How come energy is always conserved? And, most importantly, how can these rules benefit us? AS chemistry has sparked my interest in environmental issues, such as the effect of chlorofluorocarbons on the depletion of the ozone layer and what the connection between bond polarity and climate change could be. Core maths, in turn, has proved to me that mathematics is a very useful tool in modelling the environment: it taught me that exponential growth and decay graphs can be used to predict the population of an animal species, such as elephants. Throughout AS physics I have learnt important skills in experimental technique and analysis of data which are essential in engineering.

Yet nothing focused my interest in the subject as much as my recent work experience at AgipKCO's permitting and regulatory compliance department. Here I took my interest to a different level. I learnt about the process of environmental impact assessment and was astonished by how long this process takes, from the examination of the environmental condition before the exploration of oil and gas can begin to the risk assessment of offshore works. What particularly interested me was the attention to detail given when analysing the habitat of the flora and fauna of the Caspian Sea, ranging from little plankton to the population of seagulls. I was so excited by the intense focus of their work that I continued reading outside school. I particularly enjoyed reading J.E. Gordon's 'New Science of Strong Materials'. It has increased my interest in engineering as it helped me to understand the essential link between the physical properties of materials, brittle and ductile, weak and strong, and how this is related to their chemical structures and bonds. Crystals can be both brittle but hard and be used in the production of high strength materials in the chemical industry. I was astounded to find out that a material can grow its own whiskers! I decided then that I wanted to pursue engineering as a career.

Indeed, I have taken every opportunity to learn about engineering and its impact on a global level. In 2008 I attended the Global Young Leaders Conference in the USA where I took part in the Model UN, representing India. GYLC has introduced me to the importance of international relations when proposing a common resolution to environmental problems such as global warming. I realised the significant connection between geopolitical issues and environmental engineering during the debates I took part in. These kinds of activities have demonstrated to me the importance of teamwork.

GYLC then led on to my being invited to the Presidential Youth Inaugural Conference for Barack Obama and receiving the Certificate of Ecological Hope for active participation in the scope of sustainable development from the Ministry of Environmental Protection of Kazakhstan. I have also been involved in a wide range of school events, such as the high school graduate ceremony as the narrator of the show and as a performer in an Italian dance team on intercultural awareness day. I have been playing the piano for more than eight years and have often performed Kazakh compositions on national holidays at school celebrations.

My belief is that there is still much more to explore and many questions to ask in the world of science and I am very excited to embark on a degree in engineering and ready to take up the challenge it poses. I am looking forward to solving environmental issues, and perhaps, sometime in the future, I will carry out my own environmental impact assessment.

Personal statement 3

Character count (with spaces): 3,869

I believe the modern world would be nothing without the breakthroughs engineers and scientists have made. I want to be a part of this process. I always pulled radios and watches apart, but it was aeroplanes that first drew me to science. I remember sitting by the window, grinning as the wing flaps flexed, while other passengers gripped the armrests and whispered prayers. I couldn't understand how anyone was afraid of flight. I am intrigued by how devices work, from simple electric motors to the principles of winglets on aeroplane wings, and by machines and systems, especially those that are theoretical or even fantastical.

I became interested in physics outside the classroom a couple of years ago. I've spent a lot of time reading ('New Scientist' and various websites) about mechanical processes, such as internal combustion, motorbikes' counter-steering, water saws, artificial gravity in space, and astro-engineering, especially Lagrange points and space elevators. I am following the efforts of the Japan Space Elevator Association to begin design and production. I find the progress being made in the field of nuclear fusion inspiring, especially after seeing a documentary on the development of HiPER. The use of lasers and mirrors was revelatory: the idea that a power station could create MeV of energy from isotopes in sea water seemed like science fiction but wasn't. I plan to visit the construction site of ITER next year to explore the practical side of nuclear physics and see how the theory I've learnt is applied in the real world. I heard a great Design London talk at Imperial College by Dick Powell about the connections between creative thinking, design and real world applications. Part of my desire to be an engineer comes from the solutions that science can provide – clean and sustainable energy, for example, especially in light of the BP crisis in the Gulf of Mexico; or safety and recovery issues highlighted by the stunning rescue of the Chilean miners. There is such a range of exciting projects; from the LHC at CERN, which I visited on a school trip, where I first began to understand that, while in theory nuclear physics happened on a small scale, the real world applications were massive; to the inventiveness of the 'barefoot engineers', like William Kamkwamba, who built a wind-powered generator, using bicycle parts, plastic pipes and simple motors.

My interest in RE and ancient cultures (the ethics and philosophy behind science) has broadened my interest in engineering by adding a sociological element. I have been lucky enough to travel widely, and seen several impressive engineering achievements; the Sydney Opera House and the Harbour Bridge are two I will never forget. Jorn Utzon's ingenious interlocking shells showed me how design and practical engineering are so interdependent – a life-altering moment. Recently travelling in Israel and witnessing the huge Jewish settlements erected in months rather than years was amazing. Trekking to the ancient city of Petra in Jordan, carved out of mountains, made me understand that even 2,000 years ago the principles of engineering and design were just as vital and universal as they are now.

I was an intern at the design company Public Creative, indexing, using Photoshop and developing my people skills. In this gap year I have planned work experience for WSP Group, as well as at Meggitt and Classic Aero Engineering, restoring a Spitfire and a Hurricane.

Music is another passion: playing saxophone in the school jazz band for 10 years meant lots of concerts at school, the Eisteddfod, in London and Paris. I am a good listener and team player. I enjoyed volunteering at a local primary school and helping children to read.

I am fascinated by the principles and practice of engineering and look forward to the challenge and excitement that university life will bring.

Personal statement 4

Character count (with spaces): 3,454

Engineering plays a role in everything we do in society, from building infrastructure to making our lives easier, for example through electronics. I hope that in my future as an engineer I will have the chance to play a role in making an impact on the way we move forward in these challenging times.

I have always been intrigued by mathematics and I chose to take the mechanics options due to my love of physics and the application of maths to our environment, for example in the creation of new bridges. Physics has given me a foundation for engineering and it has also enabled me to improve on my practical skills and my ability to minimise errors, a skill which I have appreciated during my A level course. Books such as 'The New Science of Strong Materials: Or Why Things Don't Fall Through the Floor' by J.E. Gordon and programmes about engineering feats are very thought-provoking and educational. Attending lectures and day courses at Imperial College London and at UCL increased my interest in science and engineering as they broadened my knowledge of maths and physics and their usefulness to the structures we see around us, such as studying the way different forces interact on an object.

I have volunteered at the Royal Institution during their family fun days for the last two years and I am an assistant teacher for the mathematics master classes for Year Nines also run by the RI, both of which have allowed me to work as a team member with new people and look at science and mathematics from a variety of different academic levels. Communicating ideas is a very useful skill to any engineer as it is always necessary to be able to work as a team and ensure each person's role comes together. I have been debating since Year Nine, during which time I have entered the Rotary Club Debating competition and participated in school debating competitions, all of which have improved my team-working skills and also my confidence as a public speaker, especially when marketing ideas. As a senior prefect at both my previous schools, I have been able to experience a sense of greater responsibility towards others that has enhanced my ability to collaborate with people. I was also editor of the Sacred Heart High School newsletter, where I managed to raise enough money to expand the scale and scope of the paper.

Being able to communicate in Spanish is a useful skill which I will be using to do a four-week placement at the department of toxicology at the University of Seville, where I will be studying and researching about the contamination of the sea by cities' residual waters. Working in Spanish will be a very useful skill to me as an engineer as it will allow me to communicate and work with people abroad. Additionally, I have organised placements with engineering companies, such as Amec and Arup, in order to gain more work experience over next Easter and summer. I have participated in three French exchanges during the last four years which have allowed me to maintain a basic level of French, a skill I hope to improve at university.

I am interested in studying civil engineering as I would like my role as an engineer to have a positive effect on altering our lives, while sustaining our environment. This is the reason that I have chosen the course which allows me to learn not only civil engineering but also link it in with the environment. I am excited to start this new phase of my life and look forward to learning new skills.

Personal statement 5

Character count (with spaces): 3,311

I decided on becoming an engineer at quite a late stage in my education. My favourite subject at school was physics, and in particular theoretical physics, and this is what I intended to study at university. As part of my IB programme, we are required to work on an extended essay and mine was based around semiconductors. It was through this that I became more interested in the role of semiconductors in practical situations rather than how they work or how different types can be combined to create logic gates.

To investigate this further, I contacted the Institute of Electrical and Electronics Engineers and they introduced me to the Try Engineering project. Through this I was able to make contact with engineers and engineering students to find out more about what studying engineering and becoming an engineer would entail. And then I was hooked! Through one of these contacts I was able to do some work experience last summer, in a small start-up company specialising in GPS products, and I found this very exciting, even though most of the technical aspects were way beyond my understanding. But I did learn that engineers have to be able to be practical people because they are producing things that other people will hopefully want to buy. Following this experience, I read 'Electronics: The Life Story of a Technology' by Morton and Gabriel, which explained the history of the development of the semiconductor and how developments were always accelerated by practical requirements.

My favourite topics in physics are those related to electricity and electronics, and I enjoy the practical side of the subject very much. As part of a project organised by the school, I created a light-meter using an LDR and different colour LEDs to indicate whether the light level was suitable for taking photographs without a tripod. My strength in mathematics is also going to be very important as my research has shown me that mathematics courses are an integral part of an engineering degree. Other than mathematics and physics, I am also studying economics and art. Economics is very helpful because as well as being a subject where theory has to be applied to, and developed from, real-life events, it also shows me that to be successful, a product has to be priced correctly and marketed effectively. Art is helpful in helping me to think 'outside the box' and in a creative way, as well as a chance to use my hands to create things.

When I am not studying, I enjoy sport. I am captain of my school's soccer team and I also enjoy swimming, badminton and martial arts. I play the saxophone in the school band which helps me to understand the importance of practice and commitment, and how to work effectively with others. I am on the school's charity committee and we recently held a 'Dragon's Den' event where we offered a small sum of money to the person in the school who had the best idea of using it to make something to sell to raise money for our chosen charity (a school project in a poor region of Thailand). It was interesting to do this because we had to decide not which was the best idea, but which was the most practical and most likely to raise money.

I am confident that engineering is the right career for me, and that I have a lot to offer my chosen university both academically and socially.

Work experience

Work experience is important as it demonstrates a commitment to the subject outside the classroom. Remember to include any experience, paid or voluntary. If you have had relevant work experience, mention it on your form. Explain concisely what your job entailed and what you got out of the whole experience. Even if you have not been able to get work experience, if you have spoken to anyone in engineering about their job it is worth mentioning as all this information builds up a picture of someone who is keen and has done some research. See Chapter 2 for further information.

General tips for completing your application

- Before submitting it, also ensure you check your application through very carefully for careless errors that are harder to see on screen.
- Keep a copy of your UCAS application so you can remind yourself what you wrote prior to an interview.
- Ensure that you have actually done all the things you mentioned in the statement by the time you are interviewed.
- Research the full course content, not just the first year.
- Research the entry requirements.
- Ask your teachers for your grade predictions.
- Ensure your personal statement is directed at the courses you are applying for.
- Include lots of detail in the personal statement.
- Illustrate your points with examples and evidence.
- Do not waste valuable space in the personal statement – make every word count.

6 | Succeeding at interview

Not all universities interview candidates, but it is likely that at least one of your five choices will do so, so you need to be prepared. Your interview will decide whether you will be offered a place or not. The information on the UCAS application will have been the basis on which the decision to interview you was made, but a good UCAS form cannot help after a poor interview. So prepare thoroughly. Here are some important points to consider.

- If you interview well, and you subsequently narrowly miss the grades that you need to take the place, you may still be offered the place.
- Interviews are normally conducted in an informal and relaxed manner, the purpose of which is to allow you to talk about your interests and suitability for the course.
- Think about the impression you will make – think about your body language, eye contact and communication skills.
- Go into the interview with a mental checklist of what points you wish to mention and try to steer the interview to address these (see below).
- Interviewers are less interested in investigating your subject knowledge than in looking at how suitable and committed you are for their course. So, evidence of research and appropriate qualities such as analytical or problem-solving skills are important elements of a successful interview.
- Remember your future teacher or lecturer might be among the people interviewing you. Enthusiasm and a genuine commitment to your subject are extremely important attitudes to convey.
- An ability to think on your feet is vital – engineering is about problem solving. Don't try to memorise potential answers or responses, but be prepared to expand on things you have mentioned in the personal statement.
- Important preparation includes re-reading your UCAS personal statement. Never include anything in your UCAS application that you are not prepared to speak about at greater length or in more detail at the interview.
- Questions may well be asked on your extracurricular activities. The interviewer may do so either to put you at your ease or to find out about the sort of personal qualities you possess; therefore your answers should be thorough and enthusiastic.

- At the end of the interview, you may be asked if you have any questions. Often, this is simply a polite way of ending the interview, so do not feel that you need to ask anything. Just say 'Thank you, but all my questions were answered during the introductory lecture today and by the students who showed us around. If I think of anything I will contact the admissions department.'
- At the end of the interview, smile, thank them and shake hands. Above all, convey your enthusiasm so that they will remember you at the end of a long day of interviews.

Advice from an admissions tutor

Within the Department of EEE, we actively encourage all applicants that are expected to meet our very high entry standards to attend their interview afternoon. The reason is not to test their academic ability, but to ensure that they have what it takes to succeed at Imperial in their studies. Perhaps more importantly, we want our high-calibre students to be happy during their stay at Imperial and so it is important to know that they want to study EEE for the right reasons. To this end, during their interview, we are looking for a student who is 'switched on' (as opposed to an applicant having been primed for the occasion) and genuinely keen to pursue a career in EEE (it is not uncommon for parents to push their children into this subject). We ask each applicant a few technical questions, of increasing difficulty, to gauge their limits of mathematics and physics; not necessarily related to EEE. In addition, we are looking for a confident inquisitive mind, as well as signs of weakness areas. Since places are limited, we try to find signs that the applicant will have a long-term commitment to academic life, as well as indicators that suggest that they will help to enrich the lives of those around them.

Dr Stepan Lucyszyn, Undergraduate Admissions Tutor for the Department of Electrical and Electronic Engineering (EEE), Imperial College London

Steering the interview

There will be issues that you want to raise in the interview, things that will demonstrate your research, commitment and personal qualities. Rather than walking out of the interview disappointed that you did not have the opportunity to discuss these things, try to bring them into the conversation. For example, you may have been to a lecture on developments within the electronics industry at a local university one evening and you want to talk about this. There are likely to be many ways that you can do this. You might be asked why you want to be an engineer, and during your answer you could say 'and the thing that really convinced me that electronic engineering was the right career for me was listening to Professor Smith talking about nanotechnology at a lecture that I attended at Surrey University last month'.

In all probability, the interviewer will then ask you more about this, and you can then talk about something that you know about, rather than having to face questions on a topic with which you are less familiar.

Before you go to the interview, write down a list of things you want to talk about, and think of ways that you may be able to do so.

Preparing for an interview

Preparation for an interview should be an intensification of the work you are already doing outside class for your A level courses. Interviewers will be looking for evidence of an academic interest and commitment that extends beyond the classroom. They will also be looking for an ability to apply the theories and methods that you have been learning in your A level courses to the real world.

Essentially, the interview is a chance for you to demonstrate knowledge of, commitment to and enthusiasm for engineering. The only way to do this is by trying to be as well informed as you can be. Interviewers will want to know your reasons for wishing to study engineering and the best way to demonstrate this is with examples of things you have seen, read about or researched. Later in the chapter there is a section on current issues that you can use to kick-start your reading.

Newspapers and magazines

Before your interview it is vital that you are aware of current affairs that relate to the course for which you are being interviewed. The *New Scientist* will give you a good grasp of scientific and engineering developments, as will reading the science sections of the broadsheet newspapers. You should also keep up to date with current affairs in general.

Magazines can be an important source of comment on current issues and deeper analysis. There are many specialist engineering publications, such as *The Engineer*, *New Civil Engineer* and *Aviation Week*. Further details can be found in Chapter 11.

Television and radio

It is also important to watch or listen to the news every day, again paying particular attention to news about scientific and engineering issues.

Documentaries and programmes about engineering projects can be enormously helpful in showing how what you are studying is applied to actual situations and events. Keep an eye on the television schedules for programmes or series on anything related to your field of interest, which could range from those aimed at a wide audience (*Grand Designs*, *James May's Big Ideas* and *Richard Hammond's Engineering Connections*) to more factual programmes such as *Horizon*. BBC Radio 4's series *Frontiers* and *Material World* are also very useful.

The internet

A wealth of easily accessible, continually updated and useful information is, it goes without saying, available on the internet. Given the ease with which information can be accessed, there is really no excuse for not being able to keep up to date with relevant current issues. Radio programmes can be downloaded as podcasts and listened to at times convenient to you; the BBC's iPlayer gives access to current affairs and documentary programmes for up to a week after they have been broadcast; iTunes U gives free access to thousands of lectures and presentations from universities around the world; newspapers can be read online . . . the list is endless. In this age of information overload, anyone who is serious about keeping abreast of current issues (or wants to be seen as being serious) has unlimited opportunities to do so. Thus, an interviewer is not going to be impressed with a student who claims that he or she has been too busy to know what is happening in his or her chosen areas of interest.

- Subscribe to podcasts and download them regularly. BBC podcasts, which are free, include *Discovery*, *Science in Action* and *Material World*.
- Check online news websites every day to read the latest news stories.
- If you cannot buy a newspaper every day, look at an online version, for example www.guardian.co.uk.

Examples of your areas of interest

One way to make an interview a success is to illustrate the points you are making with examples. It is also easier to talk about something you know about rather than trying to talk in general terms. And if the examples you use are interesting, the interviewer may well want to talk about them rather than ask you the next question on his or her list. But remember, this will only work if you have done your research beforehand. There is nothing worse in an interview than a conversation along the lines of:

You: One of the things that inspired me to study civil engineering was a journey with my parents up the east coast of England, when we crossed the Humber Bridge, the first suspension bridge I had ever seen at first hand.

Interviewer: I see. Can you tell me something about the reasons for building a suspension bridge there rather than a more traditional bridge?

You: Sorry, I don't know.

A better answer would have been:

You: The Humber estuary is used for shipping, and because of the width of the estuary, a traditional beam or cantilever structure would not have been able to span the space between the banks. Also, suspension bridges have some flexibility and that area is prone to high winds.

The interviewer might then have gone on to discuss the types of forces that are present in a suspension bridge, and about suitable materials, all of which you would be familiar with because you had anticipated this response and had prepared for it.

Here are some ideas to use as examples to illustrate points you want to make:

- names and construction details of a few buildings, bridges, etc.
- examples of machines that you can discuss (cars, aircraft, wind turbines, etc.)
- an industrial chemical process
- a medical breakthrough that was developed by engineers (such as computerised tomography (CT) scanners)
- the background on the development of, for example, solid state memory for computers
- developments in energy sources such as fuel cells or hybrid motors
- the changing face of computing – from mainframe computers to smartphones.

The interview

Interview questions are likely to test your knowledge of engineering projects and developments in the real world, since, unlike some theoretical science subjects, engineering is a practical subject aimed at making the world a better place. It is important that your answers are delivered in appropriate language. You will impress interviewers with fluent use of precise technical terms, and thus detailed knowledge of the definitions of words and phrases used in engineering is essential. Potential electrical engineers need to know the technical and microscopic differences between semiconductors and insulators, and to be able to differentiate clearly between electric charge and current; and if you are interested in materials or civil engineering, you need to use words such as stress, strain, elasticity, strength, toughness and stiffness with their scientific, rather than their everyday, meanings.

One popular question is to ask which topics you have enjoyed studying at school. Be prepared for this by doing some revision so that you are not desperately trying to remember details from things you studied a year ago. Try to talk about something that is closely linked to engineering.

You may be asked about your future career plans. If you are applying for a particular field of engineering then your future area of specialty will be apparent, but you may be applying for a general engineering course, or one where you only specialise in the second year, so be prepared to talk about your plans. You may have ideas about where you want to work, in a big company or possibly overseas. It is a good idea to relate your possible plans to research you have done, or to your work experience. It is also a good idea to demonstrate a knowledge of how you gain Chartered Engineer status (see page 101).

You may be asked questions that appear to want your opinion on a recent development or issue. This type of question is asked to see whether you have been thinking about engineering issues, or whether you have been keeping up to date with current issues. Ultimately, the interviewer is not really interested in your opinion but in your ability to formulate arguments and your interest in the field.

Practice of interview situations, like most other things in life, will make you better prepared, less nervous and more confident. Arrange mock interviews with teachers, friends of your family, or with careers advisers.

Some things that can adversely affect the interview include:

- arriving late and flustered
- being unable to talk about things mentioned in the personal statement
- not listening to the question carefully before answering
- interrupting the interviewer.

50 sample interview questions

1. What first started your interest in engineering?
2. Why do you want to be an engineer?
3. What qualities does it take to be a successful engineer?
4. What have you done to investigate engineering as a course?
5. What have you done to investigate engineering as a career?
6. What field of engineering particularly interests you?
7. What is the difference between science and engineering?
8. What is the difference between science and technology?

9. Give me a very brief outline of the key engineering developments of the twentieth/twenty-first century.
10. What do you consider to be the most significant engineering project in history?
11. Do you have an engineering hero/heroine?
12. What did you learn from your work experience at X Enterprises?
13. How does the structure of a metal determine its properties?
14. Why does the molecular structure of wood make it suitable for some building projects but not others?
15. What is the difference between a 'tough' material and a 'strong' material?
16. What do we mean by potential difference?
17. What is the difference between charge and current?
18. How did the invention of the silicon chip revolutionise communication?
19. How does the internet work?
20. What is a robot?
21. In what situation do you think the distinction between artificial and human intelligence becomes indistinguishable?
22. Why are the concrete girders used to construct buildings 'T' shaped in cross-section?
23. Can you explain what is meant by 'proof by induction'?
24. Can a scientific theory ever be proved?
25. What is meant by conservation of energy?
26. Murphy's law says that whatever can go wrong will go wrong; for example, if you drop a piece of bread that has jam on one side on the floor, it will always fall with the jam side down. How would you go about verifying Murphy's law?
27. Which parts of the electromagnetic spectrum can humans detect?
28. What is a machine?
29. What is a computer?
30. What is a bit and what is a byte?
31. What is 27 in binary? What would it be in a system based on the number 4 rather than 2? Or in a number system based on the number 9?
32. Why is nanotechnology so called?
33. How does a car engine work?
34. Why is the distance that an electric vehicle can travel so small compared with a petrol-fuelled vehicle?
35. What is a semiconductor?
36. How does an aircraft stay in the air when it is more dense than air?
37. What is meant by the words 'digital' and 'analogue' when describing communication systems such as TV signals?

38. People describe new inventions as being the most significant since 'the invention of the wheel'. How do you think the wheel was invented?

39. People describe a good idea as being 'the best thing since sliced bread' – what are the advantages and disadvantages of sliced bread?

40. Why does a bicycle have gears?

41. How does the car braking system work?

42. What limits the maximum height of a proposed new office development?

43. What is meant by a 'cantilever'? How do the stresses on a bridge using cantilevers differ from a bridge using a beam to span the distance between two supports?

44. An architect designs a new 50-storey office building. How might an engineer test whether it is safe to build it?

45. An architect designs a steel and glass bridge. How might an engineer test whether it is safe to build it?

46. A designer creates a model for a new type of passenger aircraft. How might an engineer test whether it is safe to build it?

47. What is biotechnology?

48. What is the Born–Haber process?

49. The First World War was described as being the 'chemists' war', and the Second World War the 'physicists' war'. Why is this?

50. Describe this (showing the student an everyday object – a chair, a frying pan, a light bulb, a shoe, a watch) from an engineering perspective.

How to answer interview questions

Introductory questions

Why have you chosen to apply here?

The interviewer will need to be reassured that you have done your research, and that you are applying to the university for the right reasons, rather than because your friend tells you that the social life at that particular university is excellent.

Your answer should, if possible, include the following points:

- first-hand knowledge of the university, for example you came to an open day or you have spoken to students who have studied there; if you cannot visit the university, then at least try to discuss the institution with current or ex-students (many university websites have links to current students who can answer your questions directly)

- detailed knowledge of the course and why it is attractive to you, or how it links to your future career plans. The course might, for example, offer the chance to learn a language as one of the options in year 2, and you could mention this as being something that will help you to work overseas. Or it might offer work placements or the chance to spend a period of time at an overseas university.

Why do you want to be an engineer?

(This question, or a variant on it – What have you done to investigate engineering? When did you decide that engineering was the right course for you? – will almost certainly be asked. It would be considered by the interviewers to be a gentle introduction to the interview because they will assume that you have thought about this, and anticipated it being asked.)

Your answer should include an indication of how your interest started (for example taking apart a radio, building a model out of Lego, something you were taught in a science lesson) and lead on to things you have done to investigate engineering. This would, ideally, involve work experience or an engineering lecture you went to. You could end up by talking about a particular area of interest (mechanical engineering, civil engineering) or a project that interests you (a building, a machine?) and possible plans for your future career.

General questions about engineering

What qualities should an engineer possess?

(Variants on this question might include 'From your work experience, what did you learn about what it takes to be a successful engineer?')

Points you might raise could include: mathematical ability, logic, analytical and problem-solving skills and curiosity. But it is important to expand on these rather than simply list them. Explain, ideally using an example to illustrate what you are saying, why you think that this quality is important. Examples can be drawn from your work experience, your wider reading, or a lecture.

Here is an example:

> 'The ability to solve problems is very important. I really became aware of this when I was doing my work experience at a local engineering company. They were making low voltage lamps for use in recessed lighting fittings in houses and offices, but in one particular building, the lamps kept blowing. In the end, one of the engineers decided that the problem must have been in the transformer rather than the lamp itself, and so he looked at where

the transformers for each lamp were situated. It turned out that they were short-circuiting because the cavity above the false ceiling was damp.'

What does a mechanical engineer do?

(Variants on this could include asking for definitions of engineering, science or technology.)

Again, try to illustrate your answer with an example or the details of a conversation that you had with an engineer:

'Mechanical engineers work with machines. But I know from the work experience that I did at my local garage that understanding about the mechanical aspects of, for example, a car engine is only a small part of it. You need to have a good knowledge of electricity and confidence with computers, since a lot of the trouble-shooting was done using electronic equipment.'

Questions designed to assess your clarity of thought

You may be given an open-ended question about something you have already studied. The point of this type of question is not so much to test your knowledge or academic level (because this will be clear in the grade predictions and exam results on the UCAS application) but to see if you can think logically and in a structured way. So, your answer should really be an exercise in 'thinking aloud'; that is, talking the interviewer through the steps to your final answer. An example is given below.

Why are metals so useful to engineers?

You could start from first principles by describing the microscopic structure of a metal. This shows that you can approach problems in a logical way while also giving you some time to think about where your answer is going: 'A metallic structure consists of a lattice of positive ions surrounded by a "sea" of delocalised electrons. It is this structure that gives metals their useful properties.'

You might then go on to look at a number of properties in detail: 'The most obvious properties this gives metals are good electrical and thermal conductivity. Electrical conduction is through the flow of electrons through the lattice, and since they are not attached to any particular atom, they can move freely. Metals are also good conductors of heat because the electrons are able to transfer energy as they move in addition to the vibrations of the lattice.'

You could then move on to other properties that make metals so useful, describing each one in turn. You would probably include malleability, and the use of physical processes to alter the strength, stiffness or toughness of a metal to suit its intended usage.

Questions that assess your ability to analyse or to solve problems

You may well be confronted by a question about a situation that you have not covered in your studies. Don't worry. The interviewer will know that this is a new area for you. What he or she is looking for is not for you to immediately give them the correct answer, but rather how you can take things that you know and apply them to new situations.

Applicants for one university were asked 'What percentage of the world's water is in one cow?' Of course, no one (including the person who asked the question) knows the answer to this. What they were interested in, as discussed in the previous example, was in the candidate's ability to approach a problem from first principles and to arrive at an answer in a logical and structured way. So, an answer of 'I don't know' would not be very useful to your chances of being offered a place.

A better answer might start with: 'Well, I suppose I might begin with trying to estimate how much water there is on Earth. I know from my physics what the radius of the Earth is, and so I could work out its volume. I could then make an assumption about the average depth of the oceans and work out their volume . . .' Rather than listen in silence, it is likely that the interviewer will help you by giving you hints or guiding you. But they can only do this if you explain every step.

When I talk to students about what they worry about when they are preparing for their interviews, they always say, 'What if I cannot answer a question?' And here is what I say to them.

- Interviewers are aware of the level you have studied to, and so will have a good idea of what you should know and may not know.
- Therefore, it is likely that any 'new' topic that you are confronted with at the interview has been asked to see how you think rather than what you know.
- Approach all questions from first principles, for example GCSE knowledge, and then build up your answer.
- If your answer requires you to draw a sketch or do a calculation, ask if you can use a piece of paper or the whiteboard in the interview room.
- Don't be afraid to ask for help, but do this by asking for comments on what you think is the right approach: 'I think I would start by looking at the forces on the body – is this right?'

Questions to show your interest in engineering

Anyone can say that they are interested in engineering, but by applying to study engineering at university, you are embarking not just on a short period of study but on your future career as well. An interviewer (who is almost certainly an engineer) will want to be reassured that you are serious enough about the profession to keep up to date with developments and engineering issues. So, questions such as 'Tell me about an engineering issue that you have read recently' are designed to see if you keep abreast of current events. How do you ensure that you are prepared for such questions?

- Watch the television or listen to the radio news on a daily basis. Read the quality newspapers as often as you can, and keep a scrapbook of engineering-related stories.
- Check websites for engineering stories. A good starting point is the BBC website (www.bbc.co.uk), which has a section on science and technology.
- Visit the news sections of the websites of the engineering institutions and professional bodies (see Chapter 11 for website addresses).
- Talk to engineers.
- If you can, go to public lectures at universities. Details can be found on the university websites.
- Watch podcasts of university lectures on iTunes U.
- Download or listen to radio programmes such as BBC Radio 4's *Material World*.

Current issues

As a potential university engineering student you need to demonstrate your interest by keeping up to date with current issues and developments. Engineering is an ever-evolving subject, with new materials, processes and products being developed every day. Just think about the rapid changes in the field of communications over the past 15 years, for example. Once you have identified your particular areas of interest, you need to keep researching and reading about them, perhaps keeping a scrapbook (either a physical one or on your computer) of news articles that are relevant to your chosen area of study, and using this as part of your preparation for an interview.

In this section, I have covered some broad topic areas that should be familiar to potential engineers. The summaries in this chapter are included to give you an illustration of the kind of events and other news items you should be reading about. In other words, they are a starting point for your own research, rather than being an easily accessible source of information to memorise prior to your interviews.

Engineering – safety and security

Engineers have to be aware of safety and security issues when they design or produce products, whether these are large-scale civil engineering projects or pocket-sized electronic gadgets. By the time you read this, there will almost certainly have been more recent examples of situations where avoidable (due to human error or faulty materials) or unavoidable (due to, for example, weather conditions or natural phenomena) disasters either affect engineering projects or require engineers to rectify the situation or save lives.

In March 2011 an earthquake registering 8.9 on the Richter scale struck the coast of Japan, causing significant damage to property. The earthquake also caused a tsunami which caused further devastation. The Fukushima nuclear power plant was damaged by the earthquake, but the reactor core was undamaged. The active reactors were shut down automatically and generators maintained the flow of coolants into the reactor core. So far, so good: the structural design of the reactor had enabled it to survive a large earthquake, and the electrical and mechanical systems had operated effectively in preventing overheating. However, the tsunami then changed the picture dramatically, because sea water flooded the emergency generators, stopping the flow of coolants to the core. Even when a nuclear reactor is 'shut down', a term meaning that the extra neutrons responsible for maintaining the chain reaction are absorbed by control rods, heat continues to develop within the reactor for a period, and without a coolant to remove this excess heat, pressure builds up in the reactor and eventually this ruptures the core, allowing radioactive material to escape to the surrounding area. This is called meltdown. And so, although the reactor had been designed to withstand an earthquake, the design had not incorporated any safeguards against a tsunami.

Climate change is an issue for civil and structural engineers, who need to ensure that their projects can cope with the effects of storms or flooding. 'Superstorm Sandy', which hit New York in November 2012 and caused widespread damage and loss of electrical power over a large metropolitan area, and the flooding that caused chaos in Thailand in 2011 are examples. Engineers are looking at ways of protecting buildings against the damage caused by flooding, including measures such as being able to raise buildings utilising hydraulic technology to allow flood water to pass underneath the structures.

At the opposite end of the scale is the perceived danger to our brains from the radiation emitted by mobile phones. Mobile phones operate by emitting and receiving electromagnetic radiation, in the form of radio waves. The electromagnetic spectrum is the name given to the range of radiation composed of oscillating electric and magnetic fields which encompasses gamma radiation, X-rays, ultraviolet (UV) radiation, the visible spectrum, infrared radiation, microwaves and radio waves. High-frequency electromagnetic radiation (from gamma radiation to UV radiation) is described as being 'ionising' as it has sufficient energy to remove electrons from atoms, and is thus able to cause physical and genetic damage to living tissue. Although the lower-energy end of the spectrum does not cause significant ionisation, it can still have a heating effect: put your hand near something that is glowing, such as an electric fire, and you will feel radiated heat (infrared radiation), and your microwave oven heats food by exciting water molecules. There have been numerous studies throughout the world to try to determine whether holding a mobile phone next to your brain causes damage, and although most studies seem to indicate that it does not, some do suggest links between brain tumours and mobile phone usage. In October 2012 an Italian court ruled that there was a connection between mobile phone use and a tumour in the case of an Italian businessman who used a phone for several hours a day for a number of years. The challenge for electronic and design engineers is therefore to produce a phone that operates effectively using the lowest possible power of radio frequency waves, and to position the antenna of the phone as far away from the brain as possible. The power of emitted radiation falls significantly the further it is from the source. This is due to the 'inverse square law' in physics, which means that if the distance from the source is doubled, the power falls to a quarter of its value, and to a ninth if the distance is tripled. So moving the antenna a small distance away from the brain would reduce the power by a more significant amount.

As well as the safety issues connected with mobile phones, there are also security aspects to consider. So-called 'smart phones' are effectively small computers that can store confidential information such as bank and credit card details, access to social networking sites and other data, which could, if accessed by someone who wanted to misuse it, result in a loss of money or personal details that would allow the perpetrator to assume the phone owner's identity. Software engineers must ensure that the encryption software they develop is as difficult as possible to break by potential hackers. As mobile phones become more sophisticated, and can be used to pay bills or purchase small items in shops, unlock your car or your hotel room, then the opportunities for security breaches become greater.

Other safety and security issues you might like to investigate could include:

- safety features in car design, to reduce the likelihood of injury in accidents
- safety features in electrical systems to reduce the risk of electrocution or electrical fires
- design features to protect workers who operate potentially dangerous machinery
- hygiene awareness in designing packaging and production processes in the food industry
- the design of medical equipment in order to protect or safeguard the patient or the medical staff.

Engineering and the environment

Almost everything that engineers produce, design or operate has a potential impact on the environment. Some large-scale projects have an obvious effect – a new dam, wind farms, new housing or office developments. Cars and aeroplanes produce emissions as a result of converting fuel into kinetic energy. Power stations produce electricity from fossil fuels or nuclear reactions and the by-products of these can be harmful to living things or have long-term effects on climate. Discarded batteries and electronic devices contain poisonous chemicals. Engineers are increasingly having to incorporate safeguards into their designs as public pressure is put on them to reduce environmental damage and avoid the depletion of natural resources and habitats.

Green buildings

It is estimated that between 30% and 40% of energy use in developed countries is associated with buildings, most of which is used in heating, cooling and electrical systems. The concept of a 'green building' is a relatively new one. By describing a building as being 'green', we mean that it is designed to be as energy efficient as possible. This can be achieved by:

- using building materials that do not require large amounts of energy to produce – plastics, concrete and metals require significant amounts of energy, whereas natural materials such as wood require much less
- insulating buildings effectively to avoid heat losses
- designing buildings with natural ventilation, such as using natural convection to produce cooling, rather than relying on air conditioning
- aligning buildings so that sunlight can be used either as a source of heating or of electricity in photovoltaic cells
- using 'thermal mass' to absorb heat and then release it naturally
- re-using water through recycling facilities.

Hybrid vehicles

Hybrid vehicles are vehicles – cars, trains, trams – that have two separate sources of energy. While the idea is not new (the moped is a hybrid vehicle as it is powered by a motor or engine and by the rider), car manufacturers are now devoting enormous resources to new ranges of hybrid electric vehicles. Hybrid petroleum electric vehicles are powered by internal combustion engines that run on petrol, diesel or gas. They also contain heavy-duty batteries that are charged as the engine is running, and the car can be powered electrically during parts of its journey. Other hybrid vehicles use the engine to compress air or hydraulic fluid, which can then be used to drive the wheels, and there are trams that are able to use a combination of diesel fuel and overhead electric cables.

What all of these have in common is that they reduce the use of fossil fuels (and so reduce greenhouse gases and pollution) and utilise energy that might otherwise be wasted when the car is running but not moving.

Other examples of how engineers are adapting to the needs of the environment include:

- the development of new energy-efficient materials, such as composites that make aircraft bodies lighter, or insulators that prevent heat losses
- electrical conductors that have low electrical resistance in order to reduce heating when conducting electricity
- stronger, lighter materials for electrical devices
- ways of extracting minerals or fuels from below the Earth's surface that have lower environmental impact
- new ways of producing energy that do not rely on fossil fuels.

Engineering and energy

Engineers use energy to create their products, and to run them. Engineers also create the structures and processes that produce usable energy. Engineers, therefore, are at the forefront of the search to develop new energy sources. As well as being finite sources of energy (in other words, they will one day run out, or, at the very least, become uneconomical to extract), fossil fuels cause environmental damage and are closely linked to climate change and global warming. Many fields of engineering have an interest in developing alternative or renewable energy sources. While there are no set definitions of these words, they generally refer to energy sources that do not involve fossil fuels and/or those whose consumption does not deplete the planet's natural resources or reserves.

Alternative energy sources that are currently used commercially are:

- geothermal energy
- hydroelectric power
- nuclear fission
- solar power (solar panels to produce heat and photovoltaic cells that create electricity from sunlight)
- tidal power
- biomass (using bacteria to produce gas through the digestion of organic materials, making fuels out of natural materials such as palm oil)
- wave power
- wind power.

An alternative energy source that is in development is nuclear fusion.

There are a number of ways of categorising energy sources (see Tables 1 and 2).

Table 1 Categorisation of energy sources based on origin

Energy sources derived from the sun	Energy sources not derived from the sun
Solar	Geothermal
Wind (heat from the sun creates areas of low and high pressure, causing wind)	Nuclear fusion
Wave (winds cause waves in the sea)	Nuclear fission
Fossil fuels (coal, oil, gas, etc. were once living things)	Tidal
Hydroelectric (water sources, such as rivers, were created by precipitation of rain, caused by the sun's heating)	
Biomass	

Table 2 Categorisation of energy sources based on effect on source

Renewable*	Non-renewable
Solar	Fossil fuels
Wind	Nuclear fission
Wave	Geothermal
Tidal	
Hydroelectric	
Biomass (since although the individual sources cannot be used again once the energy is extracted, the supply can be maintained by, for example, planting more oil palms)	
Nuclear fusion (considered renewable since the likely source would be sea water, which is effectively inexhaustible)	

* By 'renewable' we generally mean that the source of the energy is unaffected by the extraction of energy. For example, every time coal is burned there is less coal remaining on the Earth, whereas if a wind turbine creates electricity it does not affect the source (movement of air, which is caused by solar heating).

The engineers who are primarily involved in developing alternative energy sources are electrical engineers, electronic engineers, bio-engineers, mechanical engineers, geo-engineers and chemical engineers.

Engineering business case histories

Try to keep up to date with stories associated with engineering businesses and entrepreneurs. Most new engineering projects and developments are driven by commercial companies that want to sell their products or processes, and while some new devices are developed by university research departments, these are often funded by industry.

The list below aims to provide you with a starting point for your research, as there will undoubtedly be new names that will become more relevant by the time you read this book:

- Apple's iPad, iPod and iPhone
- the Android and Windows operating systems for mobile devices
- Google
- inventors, scientists and entrepreneurs such as Sir James Dyson or Tim Berners-Lee
- Virgin Galactic
- multinational construction companies such as Arup
- aeronautical engineering companies such as BAE Systems
- biotech companies such as Amgen
- oil and petroleum companies that are developing alternative or renewable sources of energy, such as Chevron
- engineering companies that were involved in the 2012 London Olympic Games, such as Atkins
- building tall structures, such as the Burj Khalifa in Dubai or the Shard in London
- issues surrounding the excavation and distribution of rare earth metals
- fuel cells that produce electricity from hydrogen.

7 | Non-standard applications

Perhaps you are studying for a mixture of examination qualifications, or you have had a gap in your education. You may have already started a degree course in another discipline and want to change direction. This chapter applies to students who may be applying to university as mature students, perhaps with qualifications other than A levels or the equivalent, to international students who are applying from outside the UK and to those with disabilities.

Whatever your situation, the first thing you should do is make contact with some universities (either by telephone or via the email addresses given on the university websites) to explain your situation and ask for advice.

Mature students

Mature students are usually:

- applying with appropriate qualifications, for example A levels, but have not been to university and are now applying after a gap of a few years, or
- applying for a second degree, having graduated in a different subject, or
- applying with no A levels or equivalent qualifications.

If you come under either the first or second of these categories, you apply using the same route as first-time applicants. However, you should contact the universities directly to discuss your situation with them, and to get their advice. The structure of your personal statement will need to be different from that produced by a student who is still at school or college. It should include:

- a brief summary of why you are applying now and what you have been doing since you completed school or college education
- your reasons for the change in direction
- an explanation of any gaps in your education or work history
- a discussion of any appropriate skills or experiences gained in your previous jobs or degree studies.

Most universities encourage mature students who want to apply for entry to degree courses, taking into account their work experience and commitment as part of the entry criteria. Mature students have often left school without the appropriate academic qualifications for university entrance in order to start jobs or careers, in which case there are many Access courses in colleges around the country that specifically prepare mature students for higher education. Others may have studied at degree level in another, non-related, discipline.

Universities often encourage mature students to apply because they:

- bring valuable real-life experience to the faculty
- can be more mature in their study methods than school-leavers
- have had more time to think about what they really want to study
- have a better understanding of the links between study and work.

The best way to find out about acceptable Access courses is to contact the universities directly and ask which ones they recognise or recommend. The engineering institutes (see Chapter 11 for a list of these) provide details of schemes that allow students who have studied on apprenticeship programmes to progress onto a higher national diploma or degree course.

If you are applying for a degree course as a mature student without using the Access course route, you should:

- use the UCAS application system as described earlier in this book
- select 'no' to the question 'are you applying through your school or college' when prompted on the online application
- fill in the section on employment as comprehensively as possible, ensuring that there are no periods of time since you left school that are unaccounted for
- ask someone suitable (your current employer or a previous teacher) to act as your UCAS referee
- ensure that he or she knows what the universities require from the referee (you can point them towards the UCAS website, which has a section on information for referees)
- send a more detailed CV directly to the universities once you have received your UCAS number (and quote this on all correspondence with the universities).

It is important to emphasise that the universities are keen to recruit serious, motivated and committed students onto engineering programmes, and mature students tend to fit this description extremely well. You will find that the university engineering departments are eager to help suitable candidates apply and they will be able to provide you with advice and feedback if you contact them prior to applying.

International students

International students are usually:

- following A level (or equivalent) programmes either in the UK or in their home country, or
- studying for local qualifications that are recognised as being equivalent to A levels, in their own country, or
- studying on academic programmes that are not equivalent to A levels.

Students following A level or equivalent programmes should apply through UCAS in the usual way. All of the information in this book is equally applicable to them.

Students studying qualifications that are accepted in place of A levels can also apply through UCAS in the normal way, from their own country. The UCAS website (www.ucas.com) contains information on the equivalence of non-UK qualifications. These include the Irish Leaving Certificate, European Baccalaureate, and some international O levels and A levels. Information on the equivalence of other qualifications can be found on the UK government's qualifications website (www.naric. org.uk).

Students who do not have UK-recognised qualifications will need to follow a pre-university course before applying for the degree course. These include:

- university foundation courses that are offered by many UK colleges and universities. For example, Warwick University's Higher Education Foundation Programme (HEFP) includes a specialist science/ engineering foundation course, taught at a local college. Typically, these programmes last nine months and involve 20–25 hours of intensive tuition a week, plus specialist English help
- university foundation courses set up by, or approved by, UK universities or colleges, but taught in the students' home countries
- A level courses (normally two years, but in some cases this can be condensed into one year) in schools and colleges in the UK. A levels allow students to apply to any of the UK universities, including the top-ranked universities such as Oxford, Cambridge and Imperial College.

Foundation courses are not recognised by all UK universities. You should check with your preferred universities about which courses they accept before committing yourself. Representatives of UK universities, schools and colleges regularly visit many countries around the world to promote their institutions and to give advice. You can also contact the British Council to get help with your application.

Non-EU students should note that they are required to pay higher fees than UK or EU students. UK and EU students have their fees capped at a maximum of £9,000 per year, whereas fees for international students are likely to be between £12,000 and £20,000 per year. Accommodation and meals will be extra. How much living costs are depends on where you study, but, as a rough guide, about £900 a month should cover food, accommodation, books and some entertainment costs.

Case study

Upon arriving at Cardiff University to pursue my MEng Mechanical Engineering degree, a lot of negative thoughts were running through my mind about whether I would be able to cope with the studies, the environment and the community itself. Luckily, I was wrong. In class, the lecturers were really concerned and they were really supportive in guiding us. They delivered their lectures clearly so that we could understand, since English was not our first language. For the academic content, the lecturers gave us a lot of information on current issues and even invited engineers from various industries (from aerospace to subsea technology!) during lectures to expose us to the engineering field. During laboratory and workshop sessions we were given the chance to do hands-on activities, including having mini-competitions between groups which we found really enjoyable. I admit that my first year was hard for me, especially when you are 8,000 miles away from home, but it turned out really well. I began to love engineering more, because of the school, the people, the environment and the support: they are the things that kept me alive here and this is my second home now!

Engineering is not just about looking good when wearing a safety helmet, safety boots and other personal protective equipment when required: having a brain and courage is more important, especially when you are in a field which is male-dominated. Being the only female in a group of males may need great confidence but at the same time you will feel proud of yourself – a really great satisfaction indeed!

Nur Farah Ani Wan Hassan, Year 4 MEng Mechanical Engineering, Cardiff University

One of the reasons why international students are, on the face of it, less successful in their applications than UK students (see page 8) is that they, their teachers, or their referees are unaware of what is required, particularly if they have experience of applications for universities in other countries. All of the information on personal statements and interviews in this book applies equally to UK and international students.

If you are applying from outside the UK, you must ensure that your referee also understands what he or she needs to write. The UCAS website (www.ucas.com) contains a section giving advice to referees. In general, your referee should address the following points:

- some background information about you – a brief overview of your recent education, and why you are applying for a place at a UK university
- some background information about themselves – what their relationship is to you, how long they have known you, and on what basis are they able to comment on your academic and personal qualities
- an assessment of your academic and personal strengths
- an assessment of your suitability for a course and career in engineering.

Checklist for international applicants

1. Check that your academic qualifications are accepted by universities. The UCAS tariff lists all international qualifications that, in theory, are accepted. If your qualifications are not included in the tariff, contact the universities directly.
2. Check that the level of your qualifications (grades, marks, predicted grades or predicted scores) are at the level required by the universities. The Course Search facility on the UCAS website will give you links to the universities' grade/score requirements.
3. Go to the international pages of the university websites to see if there are any specific language requirements, for example a minimum IELTS (International English Language Testing System) score. Some universities will specify an overall score only, for example 7.0. Others may also have particular requirements for each section of the test, such as 7.0 overall with at least 6.5 in each section.
4. Use the international pages to see whether there are any scholarships available to international students from your country.
5. Follow the advice in the engineering sections of the universities' websites regarding any specific information they want to see included in the personal statement.
6. Use the university websites to check the fee and accommodation arrangements.
7. If you are studying at an international school that has sent students to UK universities in previous years, they will be aware of their role in the UCAS application. The school is likely to already be registered with UCAS. If you are studying at a local school that has not sent students to UK universities, you will need to register as a private candidate on the UCAS website, and discuss the reference

with someone suitably qualified to write it, perhaps one of your teachers or a previous employer.

8. Be clear about the deadlines for applications.
9. Check whether you need a visa to study in the UK (see below).

Visa requirements

Students from non-EU countries generally need a visa to study at degree level in the UK, although students from some countries are exempted. The UK government Home Office website has full details of whether you will need a visa (www.ukba.homeoffice.gov.uk). The stages in obtaining a visa are set out below.

1. You have been made an offer from an institution that has Highly Trusted Sponsor (HTS) status.
2. You have accepted the offer and have fulfilled the academic and English language requirements.
3. The institution has given you a Confirmation of Acceptance for Studies (CAS).
4. You apply for the visa, presenting the required evidence. Academic evidence such as an IELTS certificate or examination results will be listed on the CAS, and the UKBA website will list other evidence, such as proof of funds to cover the tuition and living costs.

Students with disabilities and special educational needs

Universities welcome applications from students who have physical or other disabilities or special educational needs, and they have well-established support systems in place to provide assistance and special facilities. The services offered can help with a wide range of disabilities including sensory (visual/hearing) impairment, mental health difficulties, mobility impairment, dexterity impairment, Asperger's syndrome or other autism spectrum disorders, chronic medical conditions (e.g. diabetes, epilepsy or asthma) and specific learning difficulties (e.g. dyslexia or dyspraxia). In all cases, you should contact the universities directly, before you apply, to explain your particular needs and requirements. They will then be able to give you information on how they can help you.

8 | Results day

You have done all of the hard work – your personal statement, the interview, the examinations – and you are now waiting for your results, the results that will determine whether you have achieved what you need to take your university place. This chapter explains what happens when you get your results and, if you have achieved grades or scores that are either better or worse than expected, what other options are available to you.

When the results are available

- A levels – third week of August
- IB – early in July
- Scottish Highers – first week of August

Ask your school or college for the exact date and time that they will issue you with the results.

Whichever of the exam systems you are sitting, you need to act quickly if you:

- have missed the grades or scores that you require to satisfy your firm offer
- are not holding any offers and wish to apply through Clearing (see below)
- wish to use the Adjustment system (see page 87).

If you have gained the grades that you need to satisfy your firm choice – congratulations, you have your place! The university will contact you with confirmation of the place.

What to do if things go wrong during the exams

Occasionally, students will underperform in an examination through no fault of their own. This could be through distressing family circumstances (a serious illness to a family member, for example), illness in the run-up to the exam (or during the exam) or unforeseen circumstances such as late arrival to the exam due to problems with public transport. In all cases, you should inform the universities that this has happened to you immediately after the examination. You should, if possible, get your referee to give the details to the universities and provide documentary evidence, such as a letter from your GP.

A summary of the options available when you receive your results is discussed below.

What to do if you have no offer

Students who are not holding any offers when the examination results are published, or who have failed to achieve the grades that they need, can apply for vacancies through Clearing. The Clearing system operates by publishing all remaining university vacancies on the UCAS website and in the national newspapers. Students can then find appropriate courses and apply directly to the university. This time, you do not go through UCAS. UCAS will send you a Clearing Passport, which, when you have been made a verbal offer that you wish to accept, you then send to UCAS to confirm the place. Bear in mind that Clearing places at top universities are scarce, and so you will need to act very quickly.

What to do if you have an offer but miss the grades

If you have gained grades that nearly meet those required for your firm choice (e.g. BBB for an ABB offer) but are good enough for your insurance offer, your first choice can still accept you. Otherwise, you are automatically accepted onto the insurance place. Check on Track to see if you have been accepted. If not, contact the university and see if it can be persuaded to accept you – see sample email on page 87. Your referee might be able to help with this.

If your grades are well below those required for your firm choice but satisfy your insurance offer, you will be automatically accepted onto the insurance place. Check on Track to see if the insurance offer has been confirmed. If there seems to be a delay, contact the university.

If your grades are below those needed for the insurance offer, you are now eligible for Clearing (see previous page). Use the UCAS website and national newspapers to identify suitable courses from the published vacancies and contact them by telephone.

If your grades satisfy one of your offers but you have changed your mind about the course you want to study, you can be considered for Clearing courses if you withdraw from your firm/insurance place. Contact UCAS to withdraw from your original place. Use the UCAS website and national newspapers to identify suitable courses from the published vacancies and contact them by telephone.

To: richard.martin@allington.ac.uk
From: Jonathan Luke
Subject: A level results

Dear Dr Martin
UCAS no. 08–123456–7

I have just received my A level results, which were:
Mathematics A, Physics A, Economics C.
I also have a B grade in AS Philosophy.

I hold a conditional offer from Allington of ABB and I realise that my grades may not meet that offer. Nevertheless I am still determined to study engineering and I hope you will be able to find a place for me this year.

My head teacher supports my application and is emailing you a reference. Should you wish to contact him, his details are: Mr S Buckley, tel: 0123 456 7891, fax: 0123 456 7892, email: s.buckley@edinburghhs.sch.uk.

Yours sincerely

Jonathan Luke

If you have missing results (for example, an 'X' on your results slip rather than a grade) this probably means that there is an administrative error somewhere, for example a missing coursework mark, or no 'cash-in' code for your AS and A2 exams. Contact your school or college examinations officer immediately to sort out the problem. Contact your firm and insurance choices and explain the situation to them and ask them to hold your place until the problem has been resolved.

If you have achieved grades that are not good enough to get you a Clearing place, you can be accepted onto Access, diploma or foundation places, and then progress to a degree course. Alternatively, you can resit your A levels and reapply next year. Discuss these options with your school and your parents. Don't make hasty decisions – ask the university to extend its deadline if necessary.

What to do if you have good grades but no offer

Students who have achieved grades that are better than the predictions on which both their firm and insurance choices were based have the opportunity to enter Adjustment. If this happens to you and you decide you would like to apply to an institution that asked for higher grades, you can put your application on hold for a short time (a week) in order to see if any of these institutions would be willing to offer you a place. When you register for Adjustment you do not lose your original offer, so you are still able to accept this if you cannot find a course at another university.

Bear in mind that there are unlikely to be places available for Adjustment candidates on the most competitive courses, but it is still worth having a look if you are in this situation.

Retaking your A levels

If you decide to retake your A levels, it is likely that the examination requirements of your course will be higher than first time round. Most AS and some A2 units can be taken in January sittings, and some boards offer other sittings. This means that a January retake is often technically possible, although you should check carefully before taking up this option, since there may be complications because of, for example, coursework.

The timescale for your retake will depend on:

- the grades you obtained first time
- the availability of syllabuses in the January round of examinations.

If you simply need to improve one subject by one or two grades and can retake the exam on the same syllabus in January, then the short retake course is the logical option.

If, on the other hand, your grades were DDE and you took your exams through a board that has no mid-year retakes for the units you require, you probably need to spend another year on your retakes. One-year courses are realistically the only option for students who do not achieve the required scores in IB or grades in the Cambridge Pre-University examinations.

Speak to your teachers about the implications of retaking your exams. Some independent sixth-form colleges provide specialist advice and teaching for students. Interviews to discuss this are free and carry no obligation to enrol on a course, so it is worth taking the time to talk to their staff before you embark on A level retakes. Many further education colleges also offer (usually one-year) retake courses, and some schools will allow students to return to resit subjects, either as external examination candidates or by repeating a year.

Reapplying

Universities are usually happy to consider students who are reapplying, either because they did not get the required grades first time around, or because they did not receive any offers of places. It is worth contacting the university to check whether this is the case. Some will have policies on grade requirements for retake candidates, while others might ask for evidence of any extenuating circumstances that may have affected the previous application.

Tips

- If there were extenuating circumstances that affected your application, include a brief mention of this in the personal statement ('I was disappointed not to have achieved the required grades, because my studies were affected by illness, but this has made me even more determined to become an engineer') but leave the details to the referee.
- If you are retaking, you can use the extra term or extra year to add weight to your application, for example by gaining more work experience, taking up a new subject, enrolling on evening classes that are relevant to your application, and furthering your reading.

9 | Fees and funding

The cost of studying at university comprises two elements: the tuition fees charged by the university and costs associated with accommodation, subsistence, travel, books, entertainment and other living expenses. The UCAS website (www.ucas.com) has full details of fees and support arrangements. This chapter explains how the tuition fees are calculated, and provides information on sources of funding for, or other help with, living costs.

Fees for undergraduate courses

The tuition fees that you will have to pay for undergraduate courses will depend on where you live and where you intend to study. Undergraduate fees in the UK have been capped by the government at £9,000 per year, and while some universities charge less than this, the majority charge the maximum fee. For UK students, the fees do not have to be paid at the start of each year. You are effectively given a loan by the government that you repay through your income tax once your earnings reach £21,000 a year. So if you never reach this threshold, you would not have to repay the fees.

- Students living in England or Wales are required to pay a maximum of £9,000 per year whether they are studying in England, Scotland, Wales or Northern Ireland.
- Students from Scotland who study at Scottish universities are not required to pay tuition fees. They will have to pay fees of up to £9,000 if they study anywhere else in the UK.
- Students living in Northern Ireland will pay up to £3,465 if they attend a university in Northern Ireland, or up to £9,000 if they study elsewhere in the UK.
- EU students pay £9,000 per year to study at universities in England or Wales, and £3,465 if they study in Northern Ireland. Scottish universities do not charge tuition fees for EU students.
- Non-EU international students will pay higher fees, determined by each university (see page 82).

Support and information

England

The National Scholarship Programme provides financial assistance on a means-tested basis. The scholarships are allocated by the universities, who will be able to provide further information. There are also maintenance loans and maintenance grants available for students living in England. Further details can be found at www.gov.uk and www.hefce.ac.uk.

Scotland

Bursaries and loans of up to £7,250 a year are available from the Student Awards Agency for Scotland (www.saas.gov.uk).

Wales

Student Finance Wales (www.studentfinancewales.co.uk) provides loans and grants for students living in Wales.

Northern Ireland

The Department for Employment and Learning website gives details of maintenance grants for students living in Northern Ireland (www.delni.gov.uk).

Postgraduate courses

Fees for postgraduate courses are determined by the individual universities, and will be different for home/EU students and non-EU international students. For information about tuition fees, go to the university websites. There may be some scholarships or bursaries available.

Sponsorship

Engineering students are more fortunate than their peers who are studying other subjects, because of the large number of sponsorship and bursary schemes available from engineering institutes, companies and the universities themselves. This is because it is recognised that the UK needs to attract more able students into engineering. The starting points for finding out about sponsorship are:

- the university engineering departments
- the engineering institutes (contact details are given in Chapter 11).

The engineering institutes or institutions are professional bodies that accredit and represent their members, provide training and information, promote their particular fields of engineering, organise or offer scholarships, and help engineers with their careers.

The level of sponsorship varies from course to course, university to university, and institute to institute, and also changes from year to year. You will need to spend some time researching your options.

Sponsorship can include:

- financial aid during the degree course
- paid or part-funded work placements during holidays or a gap year
- work or study placements overseas
- improved chances of jobs with the sponsoring companies after graduation.

Several publications giving details of the scholarships and bursaries offered by educational trusts are available, including the *Directory of Grant Making Trusts* by Tom Traynor. You should also refer to the Educational Grants Advisory Service (www.egas-online.org).

Scholarships

There is a variety of scholarships available for engineering students, such as those from the universities listed below. The professional engineering institutes also offer some scholarships – for example, the Institution of Mechanical Engineers, mentioned at the end of the chapter.

Imperial College scholarships for engineering students

- **Grocers' Company Queen's Golden Jubilee Scholarship:** For UK-home students holding a conditional firm or unconditional offer of admission to an undergraduate course in the Faculty of Engineering whose household income is £60,000 or less. £2250 per year for a maximum of 4 years.
- **Kingsbury Scholarship:** for UK-home students who defer their place for a year in order to work for a year in industry through the Year in Industry scheme; residual household income must be below £60,000.
- **Holligrave Scholarship:** founded from funds donated by the Cloth Workers' Foundation, one award is made annually to an engineering

undergraduate from a financially disadvantaged background; worth £1,500 in the first year of study and £1,000 each year thereafter, and payable for a maximum of four years, subject to satisfactory progress.

Source: www.imperial.ac.uk.

Bath University scholarships for engineering students

- Bath Engineering Excellence Scholarships – Chemical Engineering
- Bath Engineering Excellence Scholarships – Electronic and Electrical Engineering
- Ford Blue Oval Scholarship – Engineering and Science
- The Hertzian Fund Scholarship – Electronic & Electrical Engineering
- The Jeremy Fry Memorial Scholarship in Engineering – Engineering
- The Nick Wood Electrical Engineering Scholarship – Electronic & Electrical Engineering
- R B & S E Whorrod Bursaries – Integrated Mechanical and Electrical Engineering
- RW Barnes Educational Fund – Engineering, Physics or Mathematics

Source: www.bath.ac.uk.

Bristol University scholarships for engineering students

Some colleges not only offer scholarships to UK-home students, but also to international students. For example, at Bristol University, international students can apply for:

- The Roderick Collar Scholarship in Aeronautical Engineering
- The Sir Alfred Pugsley Scholarship in Civil Engineering
- The Barry Thomas Scholarship in Computer Science
- The Paul Dirac Scholarship in Electrical and Electronic Engineering
- The Edmund Boulton Scholarships for Engineering Design and Engineering Mathematics
- The Mechanical Engineering Scholarship.

Source: www.bristol.ac.uk

The Institution of Mechanical Engineers

Undergraduate scholarships and grants offer assistance to students who are about to start or have already started on mechanical engineering degrees accredited by the Institution. Current undergraduate scholarships are sponsored by AMEC and Rolls-Royce plc. who are offering sponsorship to students to assist them with their accredited degree-level programmes.

Undergraduate scholarship

These scholarships offer mechanical engineering undergraduates up to £4,000 in total for their studies.

Overseas study award

These grants enable students to study or do work placements overseas as part of their degree programmes. Each overseas study award is worth up to £750.

Group project award

Group projects are often integral to undergraduate engineering degrees. Affiliate members of the Institution of Mechanical Engineers can receive financial assistance for their group projects. The award can enable groups to attend or participate in international conferences related to engineering, science and technology, which are relevant to their group project. Alternatively, the funds can enable groups to attend or take part in engineering, science and technology-based projects or activities overseas that are relevant to their group project.

The award is worth £250 per individual in each group. The group is limited to a maximum of eight members.

Source: www.imeche.org.

10| Further training, qualifications and careers

There is no 'typical' day for a working engineer. One of the attractions of engineering as a career is that you are, with suitable planning, able to follow a career path that suits your own individual skills and ambitions. If you like working outdoors, working as an on-site civil engineer would allow you to do this, whereas if you enjoy working in a laboratory then you might choose to be a structural or electronic engineer. As we saw in the introduction to this book, engineers can work as part of a large team for a multinational engineering company or on their own in their own company. Engineers who are interested in planning and finance can work as product engineers, assessing the economic viability of manufacturing a product and then designing the production line.

Some students with engineering degrees decide to change direction after graduating. For example, engineers are highly sought after in the financial sector because an engineering degree demonstrates that the student has analytical and problem-solving skills.

The engineering institutes (see list in Chapter 11) and university engineering departments provide a good starting point for further investigation of possible careers through the case histories that they publish. Almost all of the engineering organisations have sections on their websites (often under the 'Education' tab) that contain profiles of undergraduate and qualified engineers. Some good examples can be found:

- in the Royal Academy of Engineering's case history booklet, which features a wide range of examples of the career paths followed by engineering graduates (www.raeng.org.uk/education/stf/pdf/tsz_fok_booklet.pdf)
- under 'Meet civil engineers' on the education pages of the Institution of Civil Engineers website (www.ice.org.uk)
- at 'Life of an Engineer' on the Try Engineering website (www.tryengineering.org)
- at www.whynotchemeng.com (for chemical engineering)
- on the Tomorrow's Engineers website (www.tomorrowsengineers.org.uk).

The websites of the university engineering departments are also useful sources of case histories, and they often have links that allow you to ask questions to undergraduate engineers.

In its booklet *Educating Engineers for the 21st Century*, the Royal Academy of Engineering provides an overview of what qualities future engineers will need to possess:

'*No factor is more critical in underpinning the continuing health and vitality of any national economy than a strong supply of graduate engineers equipped with the understanding, attitudes and abilities necessary to apply their skills in business and other environments.*

Today, business environments increasingly require engineers who can design and deliver to customers not merely isolated products but complete solutions involving complex integrated systems. Increasingly they also demand the ability to work in globally dispersed teams across different time zones and cultures. The traditional disciplinary boundaries inherited from the 19th century are now being transgressed by new industries and disciplines, such as medical engineering and nanotechnology, which also involve the application of more recent engineering developments, most obviously the information and communication technologies. Meanwhile new products and services that would be impossible without the knowledge and skills of engineers – for instance the internet and mobile telephones – have become pervasive in our everyday life, especially for young people.

Engineering businesses now seek engineers with abilities and attributes in two broad areas – technical understanding and enabling skills. The first of these comprises: a sound knowledge of disciplinary fundamentals; a strong grasp of mathematics; creativity and innovation; together with the ability to apply theory in practice. The second is the set of abilities that enable engineers to work effectively in a business environment: communication skills; team-working skills; and business awareness of the implications of engineering decisions and investments. It is this combination of understanding and skills that underpins the role that engineers now play in the business world, a role with three distinct, if interrelated, elements: that of the technical specialist imbued with expert knowledge; that of the integrator able to operate across boundaries in complex environments; and that of the change agent providing the creativity, innovation and leadership necessary to meet new challenges.

Engineering today is characterised by both a rapidly increasing diversity of the demands made on engineers in their professional lives and the ubiquity of the products and services they provide. Yet there is a growing concern that in the UK the education system responsible for producing new generations of engineers is failing to keep pace with the inherent dynamism of this situation and indeed with the increasing need for engineers.'

Source: www.raeng.org.uk/news/publications/list/reports/
Educating_Engineers_21st_Century.pdf

Chartered engineer status

Chartered Engineer (CEng) is a professional title registered by the Engineering Council. Engineers who achieve this status have been able to demonstrate that they have reached a high level of professional competence. Attaining the status of Chartered Engineer brings many benefits, including:

- being part of an elite group of highly qualified engineers
- professional recognition of your qualifications and attainments
- higher earnings potential
- improved career prospects
- international recognition of your academic and professional qualifications
- access to continuing professional training.

As shown in Figure 3, the normal route towards gaining the qualification is:

1. an accredited bachelor's degree (BEng)
2. an undergraduate master's degree (MEng)
3. membership of one of the professional engineering institutes
4. experience of professional practice.

It usually takes between eight and 12 years from the start of an undergraduate degree to reach CEng status. For more details, contact the Engineering Council or one of the engineering institutes (see the list in Chapter 11).

Master's courses

Many undergraduate engineering courses are four years in length, and lead to a master's qualification (MEng) rather than a bachelor's degree (BEng). The alternative route to a postgraduate qualification is by taking a self-contained MSc course after completing the bachelor's degree. Master's degrees allow students to focus their studies on a specific area of engineering. Applications for self-contained postgraduate courses are usually made directly to the universities, rather than through

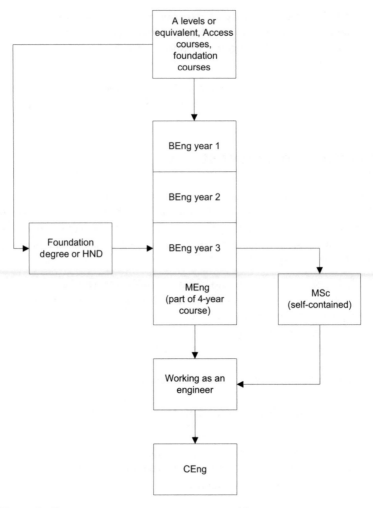

Figure 3: Routes to gaining an engineering qualification

a central scheme. For listings of master's courses, see www.prospects. ac.uk and the university websites.

The advantages of doing a master's course are:

- greater specialisation
- better job prospects
- higher earning potential.

The cost of a master's course varies from university to university, but is likely to be in the range of £15,000–£20,000 per year for tuition fees. A number of grants and scholarships are available (see page 93).

The structure of a master's course will depend on where and what you study. As an example, here is the course programme for the MSc Aerospace Engineering course at the University of Bath:

- aerodynamics
- aerospace structures
- aircraft performance
- aircraft propulsion
- aircraft stability and control
- composite materials
- experimental techniques in aerodynamics.

Source: www.bath.ac.uk.

Career opportunities and employment prospects

The engineering industry contributes around 25% of the UK's economic turnover, and employs nearly 6 million people in over half a million businesses. Employment prospects for UK engineering graduates are good, and as the UK economy recovers from recession, the manufacturing and engineering sectors look set to grow significantly. In a recent report, the organisation Engineering UK estimates that the UK will need 2.2 million more engineers within the next five to 10 years.

According to figures produced by the Higher Education Careers Service Unit (HECSU) and the Association of Graduate Careers Advisory Services (AGCAS) for *What Do Graduates Do*, published in October 2012, employment rates for recent engineering graduates were higher than the average for all graduating students, and the unemployment rates lower. For example, 66% of graduating mechanical engineering graduates found employment within six months of graduating, with a further 12% embarking on further study. Only 6% were unemployed. These figures compare with the averages for all graduates of, respectively, 62% employment and 8% unemployment. The report also highlights the attractiveness of engineering graduates to other employers, with significant numbers finding employment within the managerial, IT and financial sectors. Non-engineering jobs mentioned in the report as destinations for recent engineering graduates included:

- marketing executive
- officer training in the British Army
- commercial business analyst
- trainee chartered accountant
- renewable energy consultant
- web developer.

Source: www.hecsu.ac.uk.

In its report *Engineering UK 2012: The state of engineering*, Engineering UK highlights the higher-than-average starting salaries for engineering graduates. With a mean starting salary of nearly £25,000, engineering was the fourth highest sector and nearly £3,000 higher than the average for all graduates. As a comparison, the average starting salary for the art and design sector was £16,000. Graduates working with engineering employers enjoyed an average starting salary of £26,500.

Source: www.engineeringuk.com

11 | Further information

The UCAS tariff

Tables 3–7 reproduced by kind permission of UCAS.

Table 3 Cambridge Pre-U tariff points

Grade	Principal subject	Global perspectives and research	Short course
	Tariff points		
D1	To be confirmed	To be confirmed	To be confirmed
D2	145	140	To be confirmed
D3	130	126	60
M1	115	112	53
M2	101	98	46
M3	87	84	39
P1	73	70	32
P2	59	56	26
P3	46	42	20

Table 4 GCE and VCE tariff points

Grade					Tariff points
GCE & AVCE Double Award	A level with additional AS (9 units)	GCE A level and AVCE	GCE AS Double Award	GCE AS & AS VCE	
A*A*					280
A*A					260
AA					240
AB					220
BB	A*A				200
BC	AA				180
	AB				170
CC					160
	BB				150
CD	BC	A*			140
DD	CC	A	AA		120
	CD		AB		110
DE		B	BB		100
	DD		BC		90
EE	DE	C	CC		80
			CD		70
	EE	D	DD	A	60
			DE	B	50
		E	EE	C	40
				D	30
				E	20

Table 5 International Baccalaureate (IB) diploma tariff points

IB diploma points	Tariff points
45	720
44	698
43	676
42	654
41	632
40	611
39	589
38	567
37	545
36	523
35	501
34	479
33	457
32	435
31	413
30	392
29	370
28	348
27	326
26	304
25	282
24	260

Table 6 International Baccalaureate (IB) certificate tariff points

Higher level		Standard level		Core requirements*	
Grade	Tariff points	Grade	Tariff points	Grade	Tariff points
7	130	7	70	3	120
6	110	6	59	2	80
5	80	5	43	1	40
4	50	4	27	0	10
3	20	3	11		

*Students who register for an IB Diploma but do not successfully complete all elements can achieve Tariff points from their achievement in individual Certificates and the Core requirements of the Diploma curriculum (extended essay, theory of knowledge (TOK) and creativity, action, service (CAS)).

Students who register for individual IB Certificates, rather than the IB Diploma, cannot collect Tariff points from the Core.

Table 7 Scottish qualifications tariff points

Advanced Higher	Higher	Scottish National Certificates*	Scottish Interdisciplinary Project	Ungraded Higher	NPA PC Passport	Core Skills**	Tariff points
A							130
		Group C					125
B							110
		Group B					100
C							90
	A						80
		Group A					75
D							72
	B		A				65
							60
	C		B				55
			C	Pass	Pass		50
	D						45
							42
							38
							36
							35
							28
						Higher	20
						Int 2	10

*Points for Scottish National Certificates come into effect for entry into higher education from 2011 onwards.
For admission to HE from 2011 onwards, UCAS Tariff points will only be allocated to level 2 qualifications if **both the following criteria are met:
They are broad skills qualifications – Core Skills, Essential Skills, Essential Skills Wales, Functional Skills, Key Skills.
They are being studied as part of a wider composite qualification, such as 14–19 Diplomas or Welsh Baccalaureate.

Useful contacts

University applications

www.ucas.com

Funding

www.gov.uk
www.slc.co.uk
www.hefce.ac.uk (England)
www.saas.gov.uk (Scotland)
www.studentfinancewales.co.uk (Wales)
www.delni.gov.uk (Northern Ireland)

News

www.bbc.co.uk/news
www.guardian.co.uk

Organisations for engineers in the UK

Engineering Council
www.engc.org.uk

British Computer Society (BCS)
www.bcs.org

Chartered Institution of Building Services Engineers (CIBSE)
www.cibse.org

Chartered Institution of Highways and Transportation (CIHT)
www.ciht.org.uk

Chartered Institute of Plumbing and Heating Engineering (CIPHE)
www.ciphe.org.uk

Chartered Institution of Water and Environmental Management (CIWEM)
www.ciwem.org.uk

Energy Institute (EI)
www.energyinst.org.uk

Institute of Acoustics (IOA)
www.ioa.org.uk

Institute of Cast Metals Engineers (ICME)
www.icme.org.uk

Institute of Highway Engineers (IHE)
www.theihe.org

Institute of Marine Engineering, Science and Technology (IMarEST)
www.imarest.org

Institute of Measurement and Control (InstMC)
www.instmc.org.uk

Institute of Materials, Minerals and Mining (IoM3)
www.iom3.org

Institute of Physics (IOP)
www.iop.org

Institute of Physics and Engineering in Medicine (IPEM)
www.ipem.ac.uk

Institute of Water (IWO)
www.instituteofwater.org.uk

Institution of Agricultural Engineers (IAgrE)
www.iagre.org

Institution of Civil Engineers (ICE)
www.ice.org.uk

Institution of Chemical Engineers (IChemE)
www.icheme.org

Institution of Diesel and Gas Turbine Engineers (IDGTE)
www.idgte.org

Institution of Engineering Designers (IED)
www.ied.org.uk

Institution of Engineering and Technology (IET)
www.theiet.org

Institution of Fire Engineers (IFE)
www.ife.org.uk

Institution of Gas Engineers and Managers (IGEM)
www.igem.org.uk

Institution of Mechanical Engineers (IMechE)
www.imeche.org

Institution of Royal Engineers (InstRE)
www.instre.org

Institution of Structural Engineers (IStructE)
www.istructe.org

Nuclear Institute (NI)
www.nuclearinst.com

Royal Academy of Engineering
www.raeng.org.uk

Royal Aeronautical Society (RAeS)
www.aerosociety.com

Royal Institution of Naval Architects (RINA)
www.rina.org.uk

Society of Environmental Engineers (SEE)
http://environmental.org.uk

Society of Operations Engineers (SOE)
www.soe.org.uk

The Welding Institute (TWI)
www.twi.co.uk

Specialist engineering publications

The Engineer
www.theengineer.co.uk

Aviation Week
www.aviationweek.com

Nano
www.nanomagazine.co.uk

Race Car Engineering
www.racecar-engineering.com

Engineering News Record
www.enr.com

New Civil Engineer
www.nce.co.uk

Books

Engineering

- Blockley, David, *Bridges: The science and art of the world's most inspiring structures*, OUP, 2010.
- Brenner, Brian, ed., *Don't Throw This Away!: The civil engineering life*, American Society of Civil Engineers, 2006.
- Dupre, Judith, *Skyscrapers: A history of the world's most extraordinary buildings*, Black Dog & Leventhal Publishers Inc., 2008.
- Dyson, James, *Against the Odds: An autobiography*, Orion, 1997.

- Eberhart, Mark E., *Why Things Break: Understanding the world by the way it comes apart*, Three Rivers Press, 2004.
- Fawcett, Bill, *It Looked Good on Paper: Bizarre inventions, design disasters and engineering follies*, Harper Paperbacks, 2009
- Gordon, J.E., *Structures: Or why things don't fall down*, DaCapo Press, 2003.
- Gordon, J.E., *The New Science of Strong Materials: Or why you don't fall through the floor*, Penguin, 1991.
- Hart-Davis, Adam, *Engineers*, Dorling Kindersley, 2012.
- Linzmayer, Owen, *Apple Confidential 2.0: The definitive history of the world's most colorful company, the real story of Apple Computer, Inc.*, No Starch Press, 2004.
- Michell, Tony, *Samsung Electronics and the Struggle for Leadership of the Electronics Industry*, John Wiley & Sons, 2010.
- Petroski, Henry, *Invention by Design: How engineers get from thought to thing*, Harvard University Press, 1998.

Thinking skills

- Butterworth, John and Thwaites, Geoff, *Thinking Skills*, CUP, 2005.
- Tanna, Minesh, *Think you can think?*, Oxbridge Applications, 2011.

Glossary

Adjustment
Runs in parallel to Clearing and allows students who have performed better than expected to look at upgrading their university places.

Admissions tutor
Someone within an engineering department who deals with UCAS applications.

Aerospace engineering
A specialist branch of mechanical engineering focusing on aviation.

Automotive engineering
A specialist branch of mechanical engineering dealing with transport.

BEng
The qualification gained after a three-year undergraduate engineering degree course (often four years in Scotland).

Biomedical engineering
Linking engineering and living things.

Chemical engineering
The branch of engineering that looks at industrial processes involving chemicals, drugs, food and fuels.

Civil engineering
The branch of engineering dealing with large-scale infrastructure projects such as roads, bridges and dams.

Clearing
The period in August when students who are not holding offers for undergraduate university places can approach universities that still have vacancies.

Deferred entry
Applications for an undergraduate place for the following year, allowing the student to take a gap year.

Electrical engineering
Engineering involving electrical devices. Often taught as a joint degree with electronic engineering.

Electronic engineering
The branch of engineering that deals with electronics, such as integrated circuits.

Extra
Allows students who are not holding any offers to approach extra universities, prior to receiving their examination results.

Gap year
A year between leaving school or college and starting university, usually used to gain further work or life experience or extra qualifications.

IELTS
The International English Language Testing System. Students who do not have English as their first language must reach a certain IELTS level in order to gain entry to study in the UK.

Mechanical engineering
The branch of engineering dealing with machinery.

MEng
The qualification gained from a four-year engineering degree course (often five years in Scotland).

MSc
A self-contained master's postgraduate degree.

Production engineering
Engineering that works on manufacturing processes.

Structural engineering
Engineering that deals with the use of suitable materials for engineering projects.

UCAS
The Universities and Colleges Admissions Service, the online undergraduate application system.

ADAMS GRAMMAR SCHOOL
LIBRARY

ADAMS' G.S.
CAREERS DEPT.

LIBRARIANS
STOREROOM

This book is due for return on or before the last date shown below.

2 0 NOV 2013

2 6 FEB 2014

1 2 MAR 2014

2 6 MAR 2014

0 7 NOV 2014   WITHDRAWN
2 5 JUN 2015

10 9 SEP 2015

Don Gresswell Ltd., London, N.21 Cat No. 1208

ADAMS' GRAMMAR SCHOOL

B16528